Reteaching and Practice
Workbook

Grade 1

Scott Foresman·Addison Wesley

enVisionMATH®
Common Core

PEARSON

Glenview, Illinois • Boston, Massachusetts • Chandler, Arizona • Upper Saddle River, New Jersey

ISBN-13: 978-0-328-79074-6

ISBN-10: 0-328-79074-5

9   18

Contents

Name _____

Spatial Patterns for Numbers to 10

You can use two-part patterns to show numbers.

Use each pattern to tell how many without counting.

This part shows 4.

This part shows 2.

The two parts together show 6 shoes in all.

Circle the number that tells how many in all.

1.

(4) 5 6

2.

6 7 8

3.

7 9 10

4.

8 10 12

Algebra

5. Draw dots to show 9 in all.

Spatial Patterns for Numbers to 10

Write the number that tells how many in all.

1.

5

2.

3.

4.

5.

6.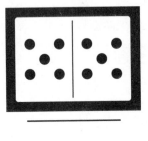

Number Sense

7. Tom has 7 dots to put on
two flags. Can he put the
same number of dots on
each flag?

Yes   No

Making 6 and 7

You can use different ways to make 6.

_3_ and _3_

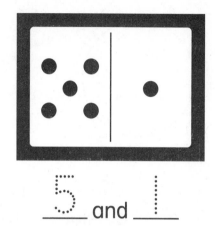

_5_ and _1_

Write the numbers that show ways to make 6.

1.

_2_ and _4_

2.

____ and ____

3.

____ and ____

4.

____ and ____

Name _____

Making 6 and 7

Write the number inside and outside.
Then write the number in all.

1.

____   ____   ____
inside   outside   in all

2.

____   ____   ____
inside   outside   in all

3.

____   ____   ____
inside   outside   in all

4.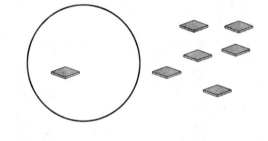

____   ____   ____
inside   outside   in all

5. Draw 5 tiles inside the circle and 1 tile outside.
Then write how many in all.

____

Making 8

You can use different ways to make 8.

_5_ and _3_

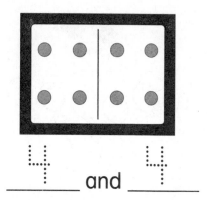

_4_ and _4_

Write the numbers that show ways to make 8.

1.

_7_ and _1_

2.

_____ and _____

3.

_____ and _____

4.

_____ and _____

Making 8

Write the numbers to show parts of 8.

1.

_____ and _____

2.

_____ and _____

Algebra

3. The whole is 8.
   One part is 3.
   The other part is _____.
   - Ⓐ 3
   - Ⓑ 4
   - Ⓒ 5
   - Ⓓ 8

4. The whole is 8.
   One part is 1.
   The other part is _____.
   - Ⓐ 7
   - Ⓑ 6
   - Ⓒ 5
   - Ⓓ 2

Journal

5. The whole is 8.
   One part is 8.
   What is the other part? _____
   Tell how you know.

   _____

   _____

Name _____

Reteaching
1-4

Making 9

You can make 9 in different ways.

___3___ and ___6___   ___7___ and ___2___   ___1___ and ___8___

Write the numbers that show ways to make 8 and 9.

1.

___3___ and ___5___

___ and ___

___ and ___

2.

___ and ___

___ and ___

___ and ___

Name _____

Making 9

Write the numbers to show parts of 9.

1.

_____ ⬤ and _____ ◯

2.

_____ ⬤ and _____ ◯

Visual Thinking

3. Which tells about the picture?

7 and 2   8 and 1   6 and 3   9 and 0

Name _____

Introducing Addition
Expressions and Number Sentences

Join the parts to make the whole.

How many black counters? _____

How many white counters? _____

_____ and _____ is _____ in all. 5 is the sum of 2 and 3.

Add to find the sum. Use counters if you like.

1.

How many black counters? _____

How many white counters? _____

_____ and _____ is _____ in all. 6 is the sum of 4 and 2.

2.

_____ and _____ is _____ in all.

3.

_____ and _____ is _____ in all.

4.

_____ and _____ is _____ in all.

5.

_____ and _____ is _____ in all.

Introducing Addition
Expressions and Number Sentences

Use the picture. Write the parts. Then write an
addition sentence.

1.

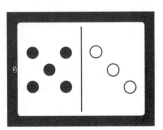

____ + ____

____ + ____ = ____

2.

____ + ____

____ + ____ = ____

Visual Thinking

3. Which addition sentence
goes with the question?
Fill in the correct bubble.

There are 4 brown rabbits in the garden.
There are 5 white rabbits.
How many rabbits are there in all?

Ⓐ $4 + 5 = 9$

Ⓑ $2 + 7 = 9$

Ⓒ $4 + 4 = 8$

Ⓓ $4 + 1 = 5$

Stories About Joining

Join the groups to find how many bugs in all.

Use a counter for each bug. Then count.

2 bugs are on the rock.

3 bugs are on the blanket.

　　1　　2

　　3　　4　　5

How many bugs are there in all?　　_____ bugs

Tell a joining story for each picture.
Use counters to tell how many in all.

1. 2 birds are in a tree.

2 birds are in a nest.

How many birds are there in all?　　_____ birds

2. 3 fish are in a bowl.

2 fish are in another bowl.

How many fish are there in all?　　_____ fish

Name _____

Stories About Joining

Solve. Write an addition sentence.

1. 5 children are reading books.
Then 3 more children join them.

How many children are
reading books now?

$$5 + 3 = 8$$

2. 7 children are running.
Then 2 more children join them.

How many children
are running now?

_____ + _____ = _____

3. 3 frogs are in the pond.
Then 3 more frogs join them.

How many frogs are in the
pond now?

_____ + _____ = _____

Algebra

4. Which number makes the addition sentence true?

$$5 + \text{\_\_\_\_\_} = 7$$

1	2	3	6
Ⓐ	Ⓑ	Ⓒ	Ⓓ

Name _____

Adding in Any Order

You can add in any order and get the same sum.

4 + 2 = 6   2 + 4 = 6

Add. Write an addition sentence with
the addends in a different order.

1.

5 + 2 = 7   2 + 5 = 7

2.

4 + 1 = ___   ___ + ___ = ___

3.

___ + ___ = ___   ___ + ___ = ___

4.   5
  +4
 ☐

5.   3
  +4
 ☐
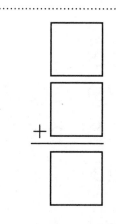

Name _____

Adding in Any Order

Write the sum.
Then change the order of the addends.
Write the new addition sentence.

1. 6 + 1 = ___

___ + ___ = ___

2. 5 + 4 = ___

___ + ___ = ___

3. 6 + 3 = ___

___ + ___ = ___

4.

$$\begin{array}{r} 7 \\ + \ 1 \\ \hline 8 \end{array}$$

+

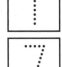

5.

$$\begin{array}{r} 7 \\ + \ 2 \\ \hline \boxed{} \end{array}$$

+ $\begin{array}{r} \boxed{} \\ \boxed{} \\ \hline \boxed{} \end{array}$

6.

$$\begin{array}{r} 6 \\ + \ 0 \\ \hline \boxed{} \end{array}$$

+ $\begin{array}{r} \boxed{} \\ \boxed{} \\ \hline \boxed{} \end{array}$

Algebra

7. Which is the same
as 5 + 1?

Ⓐ 1 + 2

Ⓑ 5 + 3

Ⓒ 2 + 6

Ⓓ 1 + 5

8. Which is the same
as 4 + 3?

Ⓐ 3 + 2

Ⓑ 5 + 4

Ⓒ 3 + 4

Ⓓ 7 + 2

Name _____

Problem Solving: Use Objects

You can use objects to help you solve problems.

Brett has 3 marbles. His brother gives him some more. Now he has 7 marbles in all. How many marbles did Brett get from his brother?

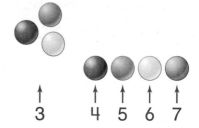

$3 +$ __?__ $= 7$

Use cubes to help you solve each problem. Draw a picture to show your answers.

$6 + 4 =$ __?__

1. Liza puts 6 grapes in a bowl. Then she put 4 grapes in the bowl. How many grapes in all did Liza put in the bowl?

$6 + 4 =$ _____

2. Keith has 7 model airplanes. He paints some blue. He paints 2 black. How many airplanes did Keith paint blue?

__?__ $+ 2 = 7$

_____ $+ 2 = 7$

Name _____

Problem Solving: Use Objects

Use counters to solve. Draw a picture to show your answers.

1. Lisa buys 8 sweaters.

7 of the sweaters are white. The rest of the sweaters are pink. How many of the sweaters are pink?

$$7 + \underline{\ ?\ } = 8$$

$$7 + \underline{\ \ \ } = 8$$

---

2. Jack puts 7 plates on two tables.
What are two different ways he can do this?

Number Sense

3. Lynn plants 6 daisies and some roses. She plants 9 flowers in all. Which shows how many roses she plants?

Ⓐ   Ⓑ   Ⓒ   Ⓓ

Finding Missing Parts of 6 and 7

You can draw a picture to help you
find missing parts of 6 or 7.
Color the part you know.
Count the circles you did not color.
These circles are the missing part.
Write the number.

$2 + \underline{\qquad} = 6$

●●○○○○
Whole

$2 + \underline{4} = 6$

Draw a picture to solve. Write the number.

1. Danielle has 6 toy trucks and cars.
   1 toy is a truck.
   How many toys are cars?

   $1 + \underline{5} = 6$

2. There are 7 cats in all.
   Some are black and some are white.
   3 cats are black.
   How many cats are white?

   $3 + \underline{\qquad} = 7$

Reasoning

3. There are 6 ducks in the park.
   Some ducks are in the water.
   The same number are in the grass.
   How many ducks are in the grass?

   $\underline{\qquad} + \underline{\qquad} = 6$

Finding Missing Parts of 6 and 7

Find the missing part.
Write the numbers.

1.

_____   _____   _____
whole   part I know   missing part

2.

_____   _____   _____
whole   part I know   missing part

Journal

3. Draw a picture to solve.
   Write the number.
   There are 7 crackers in all.
   Melinda eats 2 crackers.
   How many crackers are left
   on the plate?

_____ crackers

Finding Missing Parts of 8

You can draw a picture
to help you find missing parts of 8.
Color the part you know.
Count the circles you did not color.
These circles are the missing part.
Write the number.

$7 +$ _____ $= 8$

Whole

$7 +$ _____ $= 8$

Draw a picture to solve.
Write the number.

1. There are 8 penguins.
2 penguins are small.
How many penguins are big?

$2 +$ _6_ $= 8$

2. Andre has 8 puppies.
Some puppies are in the house.
4 puppies are playing in the yard.
How many puppies are in the house?

$4 +$ _____ $= 8$

Reasoning

3. Use the picture to solve.
There are 8 marbles in all.

_____ marbles are inside.

_____ marbles are outside.   _____ $+$ _____ $= 8$

Finding Missing Parts of 8

1. Find the missing part.
Write the numbers.
There are 8 counters in all.

_____   _____
part I know   missing part

---

2. There are 8 counters in all.

_____   _____
part I know   missing part

Algebra

3. There are 8 books in all.
Which number sentence tells about the picture?

Ⓐ $8 - 1 = 7$

Ⓑ $8 - 2 = 6$

Ⓒ $8 - 3 = 5$

Ⓓ $8 - 4 = 4$

Name _____

Finding Missing Parts of 9

You can draw a picture
to help you find missing parts of 9.
Color the part you know.
Count the circles you did **not** color.
These circles are the missing part.
Write the number.

$6 + \_\_\_\_ = 9$

Whole

$6 + \underline{3} = 9$

Draw a picture to solve. Write the number.

1. There are 9 horses in the field.
8 horses are big. The rest are small.
How many horses are small?

$8 + \underline{1} = 9$

2. Alexis sees 9 frogs.
Some frogs are on a log.
2 frogs are in the grass.
How many frogs are on the log?

$2 + \_\_\_\_ = 9$

Reasoning

3. Sam has 9 balloons.
He has one more red balloon
than he has blue balloons.
Write the number sentence.

$\_\_\_\_\_ + \_\_\_\_\_ = 9$

R 2·3

Finding Missing Parts of 9

1. Find the missing part.
Complete the model.
Then write the numbers.

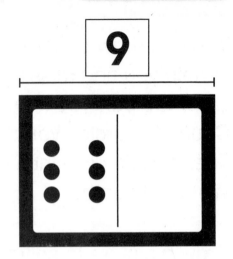

| 9 |

_____   _____
part I know   missing part

---

2. Maria sees 9 boats.
7 boats are in the water.
How many boats are **not**
in the water?

_____ boats

Journal

3. There are 9 apples in all.
Draw some on the tree.
Draw the rest of the apples
on the ground.

Write the numbers.

_____ apples on the tree

_____ apples on the ground

Introducing Subtraction Expressions and Number Sentences

Write the parts. Then you can write a subtraction sentence to find how many are left.

___5___ take away ___2___

___5___ minus ___2___ equals ___3___.

5 — 2 = 3

These are the parts.

This is a subtraction sentence.

Write the parts. Then write a subtraction sentence.

1.

___ — ___

4 minus 1 equals ___3___.

___ — ___ = ___

2.

___ — ___

7 minus 4 equals ____.

___ — ___ = ___

Journal

3. Draw a picture that shows subtraction.

Write a subtraction sentence that tells about your picture.

Introducing Subtraction Expressions and Number Sentences

First write the parts. Then write a subtraction sentence.

1.

$$6 - 2$$

___ − ___ = ___

2.

___ − ___

___ − ___ = ___

3.

___ − ___

___ − ___ = ___

4.

___ − ___

___ − ___ = ___

Number Sense

5. Draw the missing dots.
Which subtraction sentence
tells about the model?

9

Ⓐ $9 - 2 = 7$

Ⓑ $9 - 5 = 4$

Ⓒ $9 - 6 = 3$

Ⓓ $5 - 4 = 1$

Stories About Taking Away

There are 6 birds on the branch.
4 birds fly away.
How many birds are left?

You need to find how many birds are left.
Write a subtraction sentence to find
how many birds are left.

$$6 - 4 = 2$$

Check to see if your answer makes sense.

Write a subtraction sentence to answer
each question.

1. There are 8 marbles
in the bag.
3 marbles roll out.
How many marbles
are left in the bag?

___ − ___ = ___

....

2. Mary has 10 pencils.
She gives 4 pencils to Jack.
How many pencils does
Mary have left?

___ − ___ = ___

Name _____

Practice
2-5

Stories About Taking Away

Find the difference. Write a subtraction sentence.

1.

There are 5 children at the table.
2 children stop eating.
How many children are still eating?   ____ – ____ = ____

2.

A man has 7 balloons.
2 balloons fly away.
How many balloons does
the man have now?   ____ – ____ = ____

Algebra

3. 8 girls are jumping rope.
6 girls leave to play hopscotch.
How many girls are still jumping rope?
Which subtraction sentence tells
about the story?

Ⓐ $8 - 1 = 7$ Ⓒ $8 - 5 = 3$

Ⓑ $8 - 2 = 6$ Ⓓ $8 - 6 = 2$

 P 2·5

Copyright © Pearson Education, Inc., or its affiliates. All Rights Reserved. 1

Name _____

Stories About Comparing

Match the white cubes with the gray cubes.
Then count how many more.

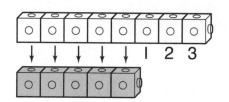

How many more
white cubes?   ____ more white cubes

How many fewer
gray cubes?   ____ fewer gray cubes

Write how many white cubes and how many gray cubes.
Then write how many more or how many fewer.

1.

____ white cubes

____ gray cubes

____ more white
cubes

2.

____ white cubes

____ gray cubes

____ more white
cubes

3.

____ white cubes

____ gray cubes

____ fewer gray
cubes

4.

____ white cubes

____ gray cubes

____ fewer gray
cube

Stories About Comparing

Write a subtraction sentence.
Write how many more or fewer.

1. Sam sees 5 dogs.
Beth sees 3 dogs.
How many more dogs
does Sam see than Beth?

_____ – _____ = _____

_____ more dogs

2. Duane has 6 tickets.
Mimi has 2 tickets.
How many fewer tickets
does Mimi have than Duane?

_____ – _____ = _____

_____ fewer tickets

Algebra

3. Use the picture.
Find the missing number.
7 – _____ = 1

Ⓐ 5

Ⓑ 6

Ⓒ 7

Ⓓ 8

Stories About Missing Parts

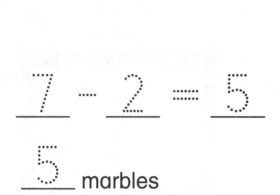

$7 - 2 = 5$

There are 7 marbles in all. How many are in my closed hand?

5 marbles

Find the missing number of marbles.

1. 9 marbles in all

$9 - 3 = 6$

6 marbles

2. 8 marbles in all

___ – ___ = ___

___ marbles

3. 6 marbles in all

___ – ___ = ___

___ marbles

Name _____

Stories About Missing Parts

Draw the missing cubes.
Write a subtraction sentence.

1. Sue plants 9 flowers.
Some are roses and some are daisies.
7 are roses.
How many are daisies?

____ – ____ = ____

2. A friend gave Raul
1 baseball card.
Now Raul has 4 baseball cards.
How many baseball cards did he
have before?

____ – ____ = ____

Reasoning

3. Amy has 9 shirts.
Some shirts are white and some shirts are red.
She has 2 white shirts.
How many red shirts does Amy have?

Ⓐ 6

Ⓑ 7

Ⓒ 8

Ⓓ 9

All Kinds of Subtraction Stories

Talisa has 8 marbles.
Some are white and some are black.
If 5 are black, how many are white?

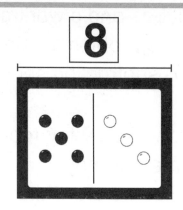

8

You can use cubes to show how
many marbles are black.
Then write a subtraction sentence
to help you find how many marbles
are white.

8 − 5 = 3

3 ___ white marbles

Use cubes to help you solve the problems below.
Then write a subtraction sentence.

I. Seth had 9 marbles.
He gave 3 marbles to a friend.
How many marbles
does he have now?

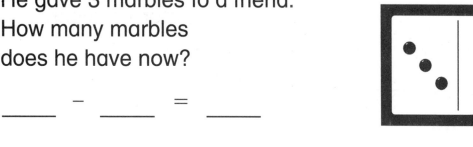

9

____ − ____ = ____

____ marbles

2. Kristen has 7 pens.
Some are blue and some are red.
If 2 are red, how many are blue?

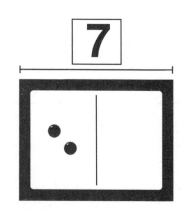

7

____ − ____ = ____

____ blue pens

All Kinds of Subtraction Stories

Use cubes and a workmat to help
solve the problems below.
Write a subtraction sentence.

1. Shawn has 9 toy robots.
   Some are gray
   and some are white.
   If 4 are gray, how many are white? ——— _ ——— = ———

   _____ white robots

2. Libby has 8 postcards.
   Chris has 2 postcards.
   How many more postcards does
   Libby have than Chris?

   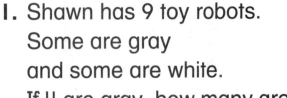

   _____ — _____ = _____

   _____ more postcards

Writing in Math

3. There were 7 birds on the roof.
   Some flew away.
   Now there is 1 bird left.
   How many birds flew away?

   Explain how you can solve this problem.

   _____

   _____

   _____

Name _____

Connecting Addition and Subtraction

4 + 3 = 7

7 − 3 = 4

> The addition fact and the subtraction fact use the same numbers.

6 + 3 = _9_

_9_ − 3 = 6

> The sum of the addition sentence is the first number in the subtraction sentence.

Write a related addition and subtraction sentence for each picture.

1.

_5_ + _4_ = _9_

_9_ − _4_ = _5_

2.

____ + ____ = ____

____ − ____ = ____

3.

____ + ____ = ____

____ − ____ = ____

4.

____ + ____ = ____

____ − ____ = ____

Connecting Addition and Subtraction

Write an addition sentence and a subtraction sentence for each picture.

1.

$2 + 6 = 8$

$8 - 2 = 6$

> The first number in the subtraction sentence is the sum of the numbers in the addition sentence.

2. △△△△△△△
△

____ + ____ = ____

____ − ____ = ____

3. ☆☆
☆☆☆☆☆☆☆

____ + ____ = ____

____ − ____ = ____

Algebra

4. Which number is missing?

$4 + \underline{\hspace{1cm}} = 8$

Ⓐ 2

Ⓑ 3

Ⓒ 4

Ⓓ 5

5. Which number is missing?

$\underline{\hspace{1cm}} - 4 = 4$

Ⓐ 8

Ⓑ 7

Ⓒ 6

Ⓓ 4

Connecting Models and Symbols

9

You can write a subtraction sentence this way.
$9 - 6 = 3$
You can also write a subtraction sentence like this.

$3 = 9 - \underline{6}$

The same amount is on each side of the equal sign.

Circle the number sentence that is true.
Draw a line through the number sentence that is false.
Then write another number sentence that is true about the model.

1.

6

$6 - 1 = 5$
$5 - 1 = 6$

 $\underline{5} = \underline{6} - \underline{1}$

2.

6

$2 = 6 - 4$
$4 - 2 = 6$

___ − ___ = ___

3.

8

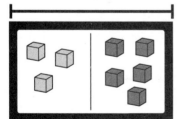

$8 - 3 = 5$
$8 = 5 - 3$

___ − ___ = ___

4.

7

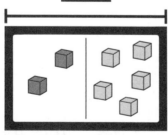

$7 = 5 - 2$
$7 - 2 = 5$

___ = ___ − ___

Name _____

Circle the number sentence that is true.
Draw a line through the number sentence that is false.
Then write another number sentence that is true about the model.

1. 7

$5 = 2 - 7$

$2 = 7 - 5$

_____ $-$ _____ $=$ _____

2. 10

$4 = 10 - 6$

$4 - 6 = 10$

_____ $=$ _____ $-$ _____

3. 11

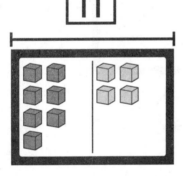

$11 = 4 - 7$

$7 = 11 - 4$

_____ $-$ _____ $=$ _____

4. 12

$9 = 12 - 3$

$9 - 12 = 3$

_____ $=$ _____ $-$ _____

5. Number Sense Circle the number sentence
that is correct.

$4 - 3 = 5 - 1$ $8 - 4 = 9 - 5$

P 2·10

Problem Solving: Act It Out

You can use objects
to show a story and
write a number sentence.

There are 6 hats.
Ashley takes 2 hats.

How many hats are left? __4__
Write the number sentence.

__6__ – __2__ = __4__

Cross out objects to show the story.
Write the number sentence.

1. There are 7 oranges.
   Jeff takes 3 oranges.
   How many oranges are left?

   __7__ – ____ = ____

2. There are 5 airplanes.
   4 airplanes take off.
   How many airplanes
   are left?

   ____ – ____ = ____

Problem Solving: Act It Out

Use counters to show the story.
Write the number sentence.

1. 9 boys are at the park.
5 go home.
How many boys are left?

____ – ____ = ____

2. 6 ducks are in the pond.
3 fly away.
How many ducks are left?

____ – ____ = ____

3. There are 8 books on
the shelf.
Dana takes 2 books.
How many books are left?

____ – ____ = ____

4. There are 4 pears.
Emily eats 1.
How many pears are left?

____ – ____ = ____

5. 7 bees are in the garden.
5 fly away.
How many bees are left?

____ – ____ = ____

6. There are 3 block towers.
2 get knocked over.
How many towers are left?

____ – ____ = ____

Number Sense

7. You have 5 buttons.
Which is the greatest number of
buttons you can give away?

6   5   3   1
Ⓐ   Ⓑ   Ⓒ   Ⓓ

Representing Numbers on a Ten-Frame

You can use a ten-frame
to show numbers up to 10.

To show 3, start at the top left box.
Count as you draw a counter for
each number.

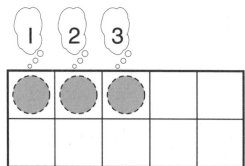

Draw counters to show how many.

I. 5 and I more

2. 5 and 3 more

3. 5 and 2 more

4. 5 and 4 more

Name _____

Representing Numbers on a Ten-Frame

Draw counters to show how many.

1. 2 and 2 more

2. 5 and 1 more

Algebra

Draw counters.

3. Show how 7 is 5 and 2 more.

4. Show how 9 is 5 and 4 more.

Number Sense

5. Kyle put 6 counters in a ten-frame. How many more counters should Kyle put in the frame to make 10?

(A) 2

(B) 3

(C) 4

(D) 5

Recognizing Numbers on a Ten-Frame

A ten-frame is made up of 2 five-frames. So, you can use what you learned about five-frames to help you read numbers on a ten-frame.

For example, the number 8 on a five-frame and a ten-frame looks very much alike.

5 and 3 more is 8.

How many counters are there in all?

1. ____7____

2. _____ is _____ and _____ more.

Spatial Thinking

Draw the counters.

3. Jim uses a ten-frame to show 5 and 5 more.

4. Bernice wrote about the ten-frame. Circle what Bernice wrote.

5 and 5 more is 10.

4 away from 10 is 6.

5 and 2 more is 7.

Name _____

Recognizing Numbers on a Ten-Frame

Count to find how many counters in all. Then write the numbers.

1.

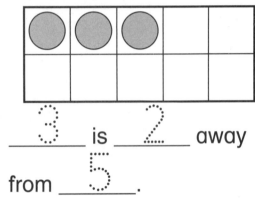

_____ is _____ away from _____.

2.

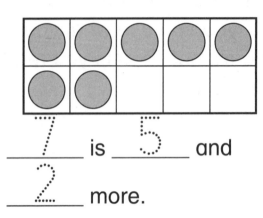

_____ is _____ and _____ more.

Spatial Thinking

Draw the counters. Then write the number.

3. Rob uses a ten-frame.
He shows 5 and 3 more.
How many counters does he show?

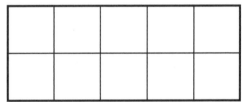

_____

Number Sense

Draw the counters. Then solve the problem.

4. Abby says the ten-frame shows
5 and 2 more. Jake says it shows
3 away from 10.
How many counters does the
ten-frame show?

7   5   3   2
Ⓐ   Ⓑ   Ⓒ   Ⓓ

Parts of 10

Here are some different ways to make 10.

7 and 3

4 and 6

Write the numbers that show ways to make 10.

1.

____6____ and ____4____

2.

_____ and _____

3.

_____ and _____

4.

_____ and _____

5.

_____ and _____

6.

_____ and _____

Parts of 10

Write the numbers that show ways to make 10.

1.

10 is __8__ and __2__.

2.

10 is _____ and _____.

3.

10 is _____ and _____.

4.

10 is _____ and _____.

5.

10 is _____ and _____.

6.

10 is _____ and _____.

Number Sense

7. Which numbers are parts of 10?

    Ⓐ   1 and 8

    Ⓑ   4 and 5

    Ⓒ   7 and 3

    Ⓓ   9 and 2

Finding Missing Parts of 10

You can use a ten-frame
to help you find missing parts of 10.

Draw the counters from
the model in a ten-frame.
This is the part you know.

To find the missing part,
draw more counters to fill the frame.

Write the numbers.

part I know   missing part

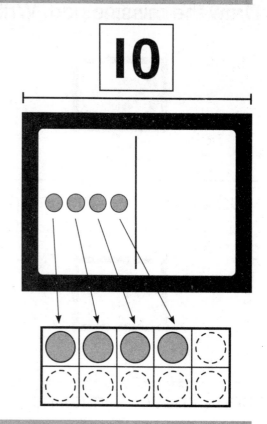

---

1. Look at the model.
   Draw the missing part in the ten-frame.
   Write the numbers.

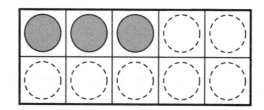

_____   _____
   part I know   missing part

Finding Missing Parts of 10

Draw the missing part. Write the numbers.

1.

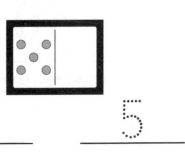

_5_ _____   _5_ _____

part I know   missing part

2.

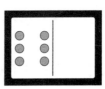

_____   _____

part I know   missing part

3.

_____   _____

part I know   missing part

4.

_____   _____

part I know   missing part

Algebra

Write the missing part.

5. $4 + \underline{\quad} = 10$

6. $1 + \underline{\quad} = 10$

Journal

Draw a picture to solve the problem.

7. There are 10 cars.
Some cars are inside the garage.
Draw some cars outside the garage.
Write the parts.

_____   _____

part I know   missing part

Problem Solving:
Make a Table

Katrina has purple marbles and yellow marbles.
She can only fit 5 marbles in her pocket.
How many different ways can Katrina put
5 marbles in her pocket?

To solve the problem, you need to
find how many different ways Katrina
can put the marbles in her pocket.

You can make a table
and then count how
many ways you made.

1. Complete the table.

2. There are _____ different ways.

3. What is the sum of each row
in your table?

_____

Purple Marbles	Yellow Marbles
5	0
4	1
3	2

Problem Solving: Make a Table

Make a table to solve the problem.

Strawberries	Grapes
0	
	3
6	

1. Ed eats 6 pieces of fruit.
   He can eat strawberries or grapes.
   Show the ways Ed could pick which
   fruit to eat.

2. Complete the sentence.

   There are _____ ways.

3. If Ed eats 4 strawberries,
   how many grapes does he eat?

   _____

Reasoning

4. Kathy has red balloons and
   blue balloons.
   She gives away 5 balloons.

   If she gives away 3 red balloons,
   how many blue balloons does
   she give away?

   (A) 3
   (B) 2
   (C) 1
   (D) 0

Red	Blue

Adding with 0, 1, 2

You can count on to add with 0, 1, and 2.

$(3) + 2 =$ _____

Circle the greater number.

Start with the greater number.

Then count on to add.

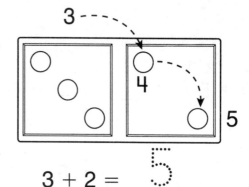

$3 + 2 = \underline{5}$

Circle the greater number. Count on to find each sum.

1.

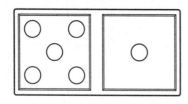

$(5) + 1 = \underline{6}$

2.

$2 + (6) =$ _____

3.

$\begin{array}{r} 1 \\ + 7 \\ \hline \end{array}$

4.

$\begin{array}{r} 4 \\ + 0 \\ \hline \end{array}$

Number Sense

5. 2 more than 7 is _____.

6. _____ more than 9 is 10.

Adding with 0, 1, 2

Write the sum.

1. $7 + 0 =$ _____

2. $1 + 6 =$ _____

3. $4 + 2 =$ _____

4. $0 + 5 =$ _____

5. $4 + 1 =$ _____

6. $1 + 1 =$ _____

7.
$$\begin{array}{r} 2 \\ + 7 \\ \hline \end{array}$$
☐

8.
$$\begin{array}{r} 1 \\ + 8 \\ \hline \end{array}$$
☐

9.
$$\begin{array}{r} 0 \\ + 9 \\ \hline \end{array}$$
☐

10.
$$\begin{array}{r} 7 \\ + 0 \\ \hline \end{array}$$
☐

11.
$$\begin{array}{r} 6 \\ + 1 \\ \hline \end{array}$$
☐

12.
$$\begin{array}{r} 5 \\ + 2 \\ \hline \end{array}$$
☐

Algebra

13. $2 + 9 =$ _____ $+ 2$

Ⓐ 11

Ⓑ 10

Ⓒ 9

Ⓓ 2

14. $1 + 2 = 0 +$ _____

Ⓐ 1

Ⓑ 2

Ⓒ 3

Ⓓ 4

Doubles

You can use a double to add.

> Both addends
> are the same.
> They are doubles.

$\underline{2} + \underline{2} = \underline{4}$

$\underline{3} + \underline{3} = \underline{6}$

Write an addition sentence for each double.

1.

$\underline{4} + \underline{4} = \underline{8}$

2.

$\underline{6} + \underline{} = \underline{}$

3.

$\underline{} + \underline{} = \underline{}$

4.

$\underline{} + \underline{} = \underline{}$

5.

How many coins
are there in all?

$\underline{} + \underline{} = \underline{}$

6.

How many coins
are there in all?

$\underline{} + \underline{} = \underline{}$

Doubles

Write the sum.

1.

```
    4
 +  4
```
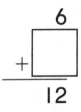

2.

```
      6
 + ☐
 ────
   12
```

3.

```
      1
 +  1
 ────
   ☐
```

4.

```
      3
 +  3
 ────
   ☐
```

5.

```
      5
 + ☐
 ────
   10
```

6.

```
      0
 +  0
 ────
   ☐
```

7.

```
      2
 +  2
 ────
   ☐
```

8.

```
      7
 +  7
 ────
   ☐
```

9. ☐ + ☐ = 16

10. ☐ + 9 = 18

Algebra

11. 1 + 1 + 2 + 2 = _____

Ⓐ 3

Ⓑ 4

Ⓒ 5

Ⓓ 6

Near Doubles

We can use doubles to add other numbers.

 2 + 2

 2 + 2 and 1 more

2 + 2 = 4   2 + 3 = 5

Find each sum. Use counters if you like.

1.

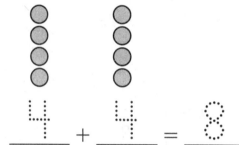

___4___ + ___4___ = ___8___

_____ + ___5___ = _____

....

2.

_____ + _____ = _____

_____ + _____ = _____

....

Write a double or a near double for each sum.

3.

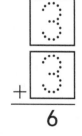
___6___

3
+ ☐
___7___

☐
+ 4
___8___

4
+ ☐
___9___

☐
+ ☐
___10___

☐
+ ☐
___11___

Near Doubles

Add.

1.   3
    + 2
    [5]

2.   3
    + 4
    ☐

3.   1
    + 0
    ☐

4.   4
    + 5
    ☐

5.   1
    + ☐
    ____
      3

6.   5
    + ☐
    ____
      11

7. 4 + ☐ = 7

8. 5 = ☐ + 3

Journal

9. How does knowing the double 6 + 6 = 12
help you solve the near double 6 + 7 = 13?

_____

_____

_____

Facts with 5 on a Ten-Frame

You can use a ten-frame to learn facts with 5.
Look at the addition sentence.
Draw counters in the frame.

$5 + 1 = 6$

Draw counters and fill in the missing numbers.

1.

$5 + 2 = \underline{}$

2.

$4 + 5 = \underline{}$

3.

$3 + 5 = \underline{}$

4.

$5 + 0 = \underline{}$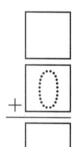

Number Sense

5. Nessa has 5 gray counters.
How many white counters does Nessa need
to have 10 counters in all?

10	9	6	5
Ⓐ	Ⓑ	Ⓒ	Ⓓ

Facts with 5 on a Ten-Frame

Look at the ten-frames.
Write an addition fact with 5.
Then write an addition fact for 10.

1.

$5 +$ _2_ $=$ _7_

_7_ $+$ _____ $= 10$

2.

$5 +$ _____ $=$ _____

_____ $+$ _____ $= 10$

3.

$5 +$ _____ $=$ _____

_____ $+$ _____ $= 10$

4.

$5 +$ _____ $=$ _____

_____ $+$ _____ $= 10$

Algebra

5. $15 + 2 = 17$

$17 +$ _____ $= 20$

Ⓐ 2

Ⓑ 3

Ⓒ 5

Ⓓ 17

6. $15 + 4 = 19$

$19 +$ _____ $= 20$

Ⓐ 15

Ⓑ 4

Ⓒ 2

Ⓓ 1

P 4·4

Making 10 on a Ten-Frame

You can make 10 to add.
There are 7 white squares and
4 shaded squares. How many
squares are there in all?

Circle a group of 10 squares.
Count the squares left over.
Then complete the number sentence.

__10__ + __1__ = 11, so 7 + 4 = 11.

Circle a group of 10.
Write two addition sentences.

1. Hank has 9 black socks
   and 3 white socks.
   How many socks does
   Hank have in all?

10 + _____ = 12, so 9 + 3 = _____.

2. Pedro has 8 marbles in the
   left pocket of his pants.
   He has 7 marbles in the
   right pocket.
   How many marbles does
   Pedro have in all?

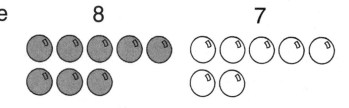

10 + _____ = _____, so 8 + 7 = _____.

Making 10 on a Ten-Frame

Draw counters to solve. Write the missing numbers.

1.   8   10

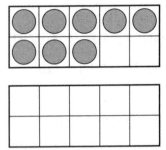

2.   9   10

3.   7   10

Journal

4. Draw a picture of 8 purple flowers
and 4 red flowers.
Draw a picture of 10 red squares
and 2 purple squares.
Write two addition sentences.

_____ + _____ = _____   _____ + _____ = _____

Subtracting with 0, 1, 2

You can count back to subtract 0, 1, or 2.

Remember when you subtract 2, think "2 less than."

$4 - 2 =$ _____

Start at 4.	Count back 2.	Write the number.

_3_ , _2_

$4 - 2 =$ _2_

Count back to subtract 0, 1, or 2.
Use counters if you like.

1.   6

Count back 2.

_5_ , _____

Write the number.

$6 - 2 =$ _____

2.

9

Count back 1.

_____

Write the number.

$9 - 1 =$ _____

3.   10

Count back 0.

_____

Write the number.

$10 - 0 =$ _____

Subtracting with 0, 1, 2

Count back to subtract. Use counters if you like.

1.

$$\begin{array}{r} 7 \\ -\,1 \\ \hline 6 \end{array}$$

Start at 7.
Count back 1.

2.

$$\begin{array}{r} 11 \\ -\,2 \\ \hline \end{array} \qquad \begin{array}{r} 6 \\ -\,1 \\ \hline \end{array} \qquad \begin{array}{r} 1 \\ -\,1 \\ \hline \end{array} \qquad \begin{array}{r} 7 \\ -\,0 \\ \hline \end{array} \qquad \begin{array}{r} 3 \\ -\,2 \\ \hline \end{array} \qquad \begin{array}{r} 8 \\ -\,1 \\ \hline \end{array}$$

3.

$$\begin{array}{r} 5 \\ -\,1 \\ \hline \end{array} \qquad \begin{array}{r} 10 \\ -\,2 \\ \hline \end{array} \qquad \begin{array}{r} 9 \\ -\,1 \\ \hline \end{array} \qquad \begin{array}{r} 3 \\ -\,1 \\ \hline \end{array} \qquad \begin{array}{r} 6 \\ -\,2 \\ \hline \end{array} \qquad \begin{array}{r} 10 \\ -\,1 \\ \hline \end{array}$$

4.

$$\begin{array}{r} 2 \\ -\,1 \\ \hline \end{array} \qquad \begin{array}{r} 4 \\ -\,0 \\ \hline \end{array} \qquad \begin{array}{r} 12 \\ -\,2 \\ \hline \end{array} \qquad \begin{array}{r} 8 \\ -\,2 \\ \hline \end{array} \qquad \begin{array}{r} 11 \\ -\,1 \\ \hline \end{array} \qquad \begin{array}{r} 9 \\ -\,2 \\ \hline \end{array}$$

Algebra

5. Three cats are asleep in a basket.
If no cats wake up, which tells how many are asleep?

Ⓐ 0

Ⓑ 1

Ⓒ 2

Ⓓ 3

Journal

6. Draw a picture that shows 2 less than. Write a subtraction sentence for your story.

_____ − _____ = _____

Thinking Addition

Doubles help you to subtract.

Think: $3 + 3 = \underline{6}$, so $6 - 3 = \underline{3}$.

Add the doubles.
Then use the doubles to help you subtract.

1.

$1 + 1 = \underline{2}$, so $2 - 1 = \underline{}$.

2.

$4 + 4 = \underline{}$, so $8 - 4 = \underline{}$.

Visual Thinking

Complete the addition and subtraction sentences.

3. $2 + 2 = \underline{}$

$4 - 2 = \underline{}$

Name _____

Thinking Addition

Add the doubles.
Then use the doubles to help you subtract.

1.

$$\begin{array}{r} 3 \\ + 3 \\ \hline 6 \end{array}$$ $$\begin{array}{r} 6 \\ - 3 \\ \hline 3 \end{array}$$

If $3 + 3 = 6$,
then $6 - 3 = 3$.

2.

$$\begin{array}{r} 4 \\ + 4 \\ \hline \end{array}$$ $$\begin{array}{r} 8 \\ - 4 \\ \hline \end{array}$$

3.

$$\begin{array}{r} 6 \\ + 6 \\ \hline \end{array}$$ $$\begin{array}{r} 12 \\ - 6 \\ \hline \end{array}$$

4.

$$\begin{array}{r} 2 \\ + 2 \\ \hline \end{array}$$ $$\begin{array}{r} 4 \\ - 2 \\ \hline \end{array}$$

5.

$$\begin{array}{r} 5 \\ + 5 \\ \hline \end{array}$$ $$\begin{array}{r} 10 \\ - 5 \\ \hline \end{array}$$

Number Sense

6. Mark the double that will help you subtract.

$8 - 4 =$ _____

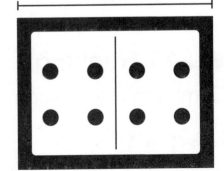

Ⓐ $3 + 3$

Ⓑ $4 + 4$

Ⓒ $5 + 5$

Ⓓ $8 + 8$

Thinking Addition to 8 to Subtract

You can think addition to help you subtract.

Think: I know
2 + 6 = 8,
so 8 − 6 = 2.

$$\frac{2}{8} + \frac{6}{6} = \frac{8}{2}$$

Write an addition fact. Think of the addition fact to help you write and solve the subtraction fact.

1.

$$\frac{2}{6} + \frac{4}{4} = \frac{6}{2}$$

2.

$$\_\_\_ + \_\_\_ = 7$$
$$7 - \_\_\_ = \_\_\_$$

3.

$$\_\_\_ + \_\_\_ = \_\_\_$$
$$\_\_\_ - \_\_\_ = \_\_\_$$

4.

$$\_\_\_ + \_\_\_ = \_\_\_$$
$$\_\_\_ - \_\_\_ = \_\_\_$$

Algebra

5. If $\triangle + \bigcirc = \square$, then _____ − _____ = _____.

Thinking Addition to 8 to Subtract

Think addition to help you subtract.
Draw the missing part. Write the numbers.

1.

6

Think 4 + _____ = 6.

So, 6 − 4 = _____.

2.

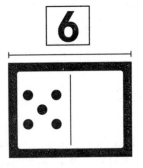

6

Think 5 + _____ = 6.

So, 6 − 5 = _____.

3.

8

Think 5 + _____ = 8.

So, 8 − 5 = _____.

4.

7

Think 4 + _____ = 7.

So, 7 − 4 = _____.

Algebra

5. Tia needs to make 8 baskets. She makes 2 baskets.
How many more baskets does Tia need to make?
Which addition fact can help you subtract?

Ⓐ   8 + 6 = 14

Ⓑ   6 + 6 = 12

Ⓒ   2 + 8 = 10

Ⓓ   2 + 6 = 8

Thinking Addition to 12 to Subtract

You can use addition facts to help you subtract.

$8 + 1 = 9$

$9 - 1 = 8$

$8 + 1 = 9$
and
$9 - 1 = 8$
are related facts.

Use the addition fact to help you subtract.

1.

$10 - 2 =$ _____

$8 + 2 = 10$

2.

$11 - 4 =$ _____

$7 + 4 = 11$

3.

$12 - 9 =$ _____

$3 + 9 = 12$

4.

$11 - 6 =$ _____

$5 + 6 = 11$

Name _____

Thinking Addition to 12 to Subtract

Think addition to help you subtract.

1.

Think: $4 + \underline{\hspace{1cm}} = 11$

So, $11 - 4 = \underline{\hspace{1cm}}$.

2.

Think: $8 + \underline{\hspace{1cm}} = 12$

So, $12 - 8 = \underline{\hspace{1cm}}$.

3.

Think: $9 + \underline{\hspace{1cm}} = 12$

So, $12 - 9 = \underline{\hspace{1cm}}$.

4.

Think: $4 + \underline{\hspace{1cm}} = 10$

So, $10 - 4 = \underline{\hspace{1cm}}$.

Problem Solving

5. Mark scores 6 points. Amy scores 11 points.
How many points does Mark need to tie the game?
Write a number sentence to solve.

$\underline{\hspace{1cm}} \bigcirc \underline{\hspace{1cm}} = \underline{\hspace{1cm}}$

$\underline{\hspace{1cm}}$ points

Problem Solving: Draw a Picture and Write a Number Sentence

There are 4 blue butttons.
There are 3 red buttons.
How many buttons are there?

Blue Buttons   **Red Buttons**

You need to find how many buttons
there are in all.

You can draw a picture of the buttons.   4
Then you can write a number sentence.   ____ + ____ = ____
Count the buttons in your picture to find the sum.

_____ buttons

You can also draw a picture to help you solve a subtraction problem.

Mia has 7 grapes.
First, draw a picture of all the grapes.

Mia eats 3 grapes.
Cross out the grapes she eats.

Count how many grapes are left.   _____ grapes

Write a number sentence that tells about the picture.

  7
____ − ____ = ____

Check your work.
Does the number sentence match the picture?

Problem Solving: Draw a Picture and Write a Number Sentence

Write a number sentence to solve.
Draw a picture to check.

1. Abby has 8 apples.
   Judy gives her 3 more apples.
   How many apples does
   Abby have in all?

   _____ + _____ = _____

2. Maya has 9 pears.
   3 pears are green.
   The rest are yellow.
   How many pears are yellow?

   _____ − _____ = _____

Reasoning

3. There are 7 birds. 3 birds fly away.
   How many birds are left?
   Which number sentence can
   help you find the answer?

   Ⓐ $7 - 2 = 5$

   Ⓑ $7 - 3 = 4$

   Ⓒ $9 - 7 = 2$

   Ⓓ $7 - 6 = 1$

Doubles

When you add the same number to itself, you are using doubles.

◇
◇ + 1
1
——
2

◇◇
◇◇ + 2
2
——
4

◇◇◇
◇◇◇ + 3
3
——
6

◇◇◇◇
◇◇◇◇ + 4
4
——
8

Use doubles to add. Draw doubles to help you.

1.
◇◇◇◇◇
◇◇◇◇◇
5
+ 5
——
10

2.
○○○○○○
6
+ 6
——

3.
○○○○○○○
7
+ 7
——

4.
○○○○○○○○○○
10
+ 10
——

Visual Thinking

5. For each picture write an addition sentence that tells how many buttons there are.

3 + ____ = ____

____ + ____ = ____

Doubles

Add to solve. Then circle the doubles.

1.
$$\begin{array}{r} 5 \\ + 5 \\ \hline \end{array}$$
$$\begin{array}{r} 6 \\ + 7 \\ \hline \end{array}$$
$$\begin{array}{r} 6 \\ + 3 \\ \hline \end{array}$$
$$\begin{array}{r} 8 \\ + 8 \\ \hline \end{array}$$
$$\begin{array}{r} 5 \\ + 8 \\ \hline \end{array}$$
$$\begin{array}{r} 2 \\ + 2 \\ \hline \end{array}$$

2.
$$\begin{array}{r} 4 \\ + 2 \\ \hline \end{array}$$
$$\begin{array}{r} 2 \\ + 7 \\ \hline \end{array}$$
$$\begin{array}{r} 7 \\ + 7 \\ \hline \end{array}$$
$$\begin{array}{r} 8 \\ + 1 \\ \hline \end{array}$$
$$\begin{array}{r} 4 \\ + 4 \\ \hline \end{array}$$
$$\begin{array}{r} 5 \\ + 2 \\ \hline \end{array}$$

3.
$$\begin{array}{r} 10 \\ + 10 \\ \hline \end{array}$$
$$\begin{array}{r} 5 \\ + 0 \\ \hline \end{array}$$
$$\begin{array}{r} 3 \\ + 3 \\ \hline \end{array}$$
$$\begin{array}{r} 6 \\ + 9 \\ \hline \end{array}$$
$$\begin{array}{r} 9 \\ + 2 \\ \hline \end{array}$$
$$\begin{array}{r} 4 \\ + 4 \\ \hline \end{array}$$

4.
$$\begin{array}{r} 6 \\ + 6 \\ \hline \end{array}$$
$$\begin{array}{r} 5 \\ + 7 \\ \hline \end{array}$$
$$\begin{array}{r} 6 \\ + 8 \\ \hline \end{array}$$
$$\begin{array}{r} 9 \\ + 9 \\ \hline \end{array}$$
$$\begin{array}{r} 5 \\ + 4 \\ \hline \end{array}$$
$$\begin{array}{r} 1 \\ + 1 \\ \hline \end{array}$$

Reasoning

5. Jack has 5 toy cars. Sam has 5 toy cars.
Which doubles fact shows how many cars
they have in all?

Ⓐ $4 + 4 = 8$

Ⓑ $5 + 5 = 10$

Ⓒ $6 + 6 = 12$

Ⓓ $7 + 7 = 14$

Doubles Plus 1

You can use doubles facts to add 4 + 5.
Because 5 = 4 + 1, you can write 4 + 5 as

4   +   4   +   1

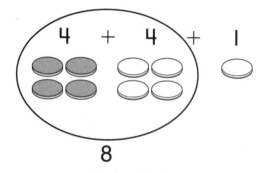

4   +   4   +   1

8

I know 4 + 4 = 8.
I know 8 and 1 more is 9.
So 4 + 5 = 9.

Add to find the doubles and doubles-plus-1 facts.

1.   3   3
   + 3   + 4
   6   7

---

2. Bill has 6 trucks.
Ashley has 7 trucks.
How many trucks do
they have in all?

_____ trucks

3. Peter read 7 books.
Kira read 8 books.
How many books did
they read in all?

_____ books

Doubles Plus 1

Add the doubles.
Then use the doubles to help you add.

1.

Think **5** + **5** = **10**.

So, 5 + 6 = _____.

2.

Think ____ + ____ = ____.

So, 3 + 4 = _____.

3.

Think ____ + ____ = ____.

So, 7 + 8 = _____.

4.

Think ____ + ____ = ____.

So, 9 + 10 = _____.

Number Sense

5. Paco has 5 model cars.
He gets 6 more cars for his birthday.
How many cars does he have now?

Ⓐ 12

Ⓑ 11

Ⓒ 10

Ⓓ 9

Doubles Plus 2

You can use doubles facts to add 6 + 8.
Because 8 = 6 + 2, you can write 6 + 8 as

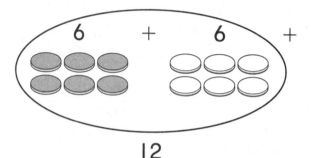

I know 6 + 6 = 12.
I know 12 and 2 more is 14.
So 6 + 8 = 14.

12

Add to find the doubles and doubles-plus-2 facts.

1.   3   3
   + 3   + 5

   6   8

2. 4 + 6 = _____   3. 7 + 9 = _____

4. Max scored 9 runs on Monday
   and 11 runs on Tuesday.
   How many runs did he score in all?

   What doubles fact will you use?

   _____ + _____ = _____

   So, 9 + 11 = _____ runs.

Doubles Plus 2

Draw 2 more cubes. Use a doubles fact to help you add.

1.

Think $\underline{8} + \underline{8} = \underline{16}$.

So, $8 + 10 =$ _____.

2.

Think ____ + ____ = ____.

So, $9 + 11 =$ _____.

3.

Think ____ + ____ = ____.

So, $3 + 5 =$ _____.

4.

Think ____ + ____ = ____.

So, $2 + 4 =$ _____.

Journal

5. Write a story about the doubles-plus-2 fact $5 + 7 = 12$.

_____

_____

_____

_____

Name _____

Problem Solving:
Two-Question Problems

Jill has 6 marbles. She gets 5 more. $6 + 5 = \underline{11}$ marbles
How many marbles does
she have in all?

Jill gives 8 marbles to Sal.
Now how many marbles
does Jill have?

> I know Jill has 11 marbles in all.
> I know she gives Sal 8.
> I can subtract to find how many
> she has left.

$11 - 8 = \underline{3}$ Jill has $\underline{3}$ marbles left.

---

1. Jack has 4 model cars. He gets 3 more model cars.
How many model cars does Jack have in all?

$\underline{3} + \underline{4} = \underline{7}$ model cars

For his birthday Jack gets 5 model cars.
How many model cars does he have now?

$\underline{} + \underline{} = \underline{}$ model cars

2. Nicky has 6 charms on her bracelet. She buys 8 more.
How many charms does Nicky have in all?

$\underline{} + \underline{} = \underline{}$ charms

On the way home 4 charms are lost.
How many charms does Nicky have now?

$\underline{} - \underline{} = \underline{}$ charms

Problem Solving:
Two-Question Problems

Write number sentences to solve both parts.

1. Peter read 7 books about dinosaurs.
   He read 8 books about sharks.
   How many books did Peter read in all?

   _____ ◯ _____ = _____ books

   Peter did not like 6 of the books he read.
   How many books did Peter like?

   _____ ◯ _____ = _____ books

Journal

Write a second problem to go with the first problem.
Solve your problem.

2. Nate counts dogs at the dog park.
   He sees 9 small dogs and 7 big dogs.
   How many dogs does he see in all?

   $9 + 7 = 16$

   _____

   _____

   _____

   _____

Name _____

Making 10 to Add

Making 10 can help you add.

Add 7 + 4.

Make a 10.

  7 and 4 more

  10 and 1 more

So 7 + 4 and 10 + 1 have the same sum.

7 + 4 = ___ and 10 + 1 = ___.

Draw the missing counters. Then write the sums.

1.

8
+ 5
13

10
+ 3
13

2.

9
+ 6

10
+ 5

3.

7
+ 6

10
+ 3

Name _____

Making 10 to Add

Draw the counters. Then write the sums.

1.

$$\begin{array}{r} 6 \\ + 7 \\ \hline 13 \end{array}$$

$$\begin{array}{r} 10 \\ + 3 \\ \hline 13 \end{array}$$

2.

$$\begin{array}{r} 9 \\ + 5 \\ \hline \end{array}$$

$$\begin{array}{r} 10 \\ + 4 \\ \hline \end{array}$$

3.

$$\begin{array}{r} 8 \\ + 3 \\ \hline \end{array}$$

$$\begin{array}{r} 10 \\ + 1 \\ \hline \end{array}$$

4.

$$\begin{array}{r} 7 \\ + 5 \\ \hline \end{array}$$

$$\begin{array}{r} 10 \\ + 2 \\ \hline \end{array}$$

Algebra

Find the sum.

5. $6 + 5 = 10 + 1 =$ _____

14	13	12	11
Ⓐ	Ⓑ	Ⓒ	Ⓓ

6. $9 + 9 = 10 + 8 =$ _____

16	17	18	19
Ⓐ	Ⓑ	Ⓒ	Ⓓ

P 5·5

Making 10 to Add 9

You can make 10 to find 9 + 7.
Draw 9 white triangles and 7 gray triangles.
Circle a group of 10. Count the leftover triangles.
Then complete the number sentence.

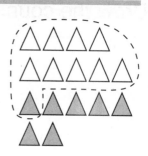

10 + _____6_____ = 16, so 9 + 7 = _____16_____.

Circle a group of 10. Then write 2 addition sentences.

1. Alice picked 9 flowers.
Tanisha picked 5 flowers.
How many flowers were
picked altogether?

10 + _____ = 14, so 9 + 5 = _____.

2. Paul caught 9 ladybugs.
Cecil caught 3 ladybugs.
How many ladybugs were
caught altogether?

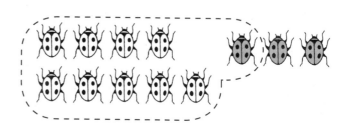

10 + _____ = _____ , so 9 + 3 = _____.

Algebra

3. Sam has 9 red pens and 8 blue pens. Circle all the
ways to show how many pens Sam has in all.

9 + 8   9 + 8 + 7   1 + 8 + 8   10 + 7   10 + 8

Making 10 to Add 9

Draw counters to help you add. Write the missing addend.
Then write the sums.

1. 9
   + 3
   ———
     ?

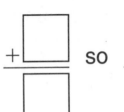

2. 9
   + 6
   ———
     ?

Reasoning

Which number answers the riddle?

3. When you add 9 to me, the sum is
the same as 10 + 10.

(A) 8

(B) 9

(C) 10

(D) 11

Making 10 to Add 8

You can make 10 to find 8 + 6.
Draw 8 white marbles and 6 black marbles.

Circle a group of 10. Count the leftover marbles.
Then complete the number sentence.

10 + ___4___ = 14, so 8 + 6 = ___14___.

Circle a group of 10. Then write 2 addition sentences.

1. Kim has 8 white toy bears.
Tia has 4 gray toy bears.
How many bears do they
have in all?

10 + _____ = 12, so 8 + 4 = _____.

2. Tamika caught 8 butterflies.
Cecil caught 7 butterflies.
How many butterflies
were caught altogether?

10 + _____ = _____, so 8 + 7 = _____.

Making 10 to Add 8

Draw counters to help you add.
Write the missing addend.
Then write the sums.

1.   8
+ 6
――
   ?

10   8

☐
+ ☐   so   + 6
――   ――
☐   ☐

2.   8
+ 3
――
   ?

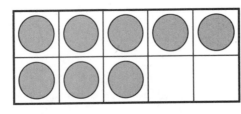

10   8

☐
+ ☐   so   + 3
――   ――
☐   ☐

Algebra

Find the sum.

3. 8 + 4 = 10 + 2 = _____

    11   12   13   14
    Ⓐ   Ⓑ   Ⓒ   Ⓓ

Adding Three Numbers

When you add 3 numbers, look for facts you know.
Then add the other number.

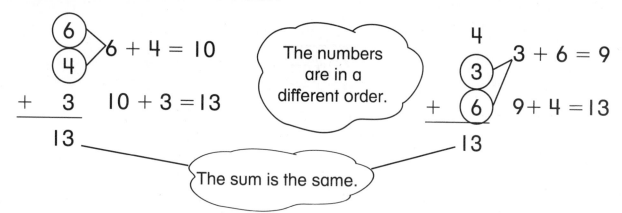

(6)
(4) 6 + 4 = 10

+ 3   10 + 3 = 13
─────
13

The numbers are in a different order.

4
(3)   3 + 6 = 9
+ (6) 9 + 4 = 13
─────
13

The sum is the same.

Find each sum. Add the circled numbers first.
Then add the other number.

1. (5)
         2   5 + 5 = 10
       + (5) 10 + 2 = 12
       ─────
         12

5
(2) 2 + 5 = 7
+ (5) 7 + 5 = 12
─────
12

2. (3)
        (6) 3 + 6 = ____
       + 4
       ─────   ____ + 4 = ____

3
(6) 6 + 4 = ____
+ (4)
─────   ____ + 3 = ____

3. (9)
        (4) 9 + 4 = ____
       + 7
       ─────   ____ + 7 = ____

9
(4) 4 + 7 = ____
+ (7)
─────   ____ + 9 = ____

Adding Three Numbers

Circle 2 numbers to add first.
Write their sum in the box.
Then write the sum of all 3 numbers.

1.

    7
    4
+ 3 ☐

    9
    1
+ 5 ☐

2.
    6
    3
+ 4 ☐

    5
    5
+ 7 ☐

    2
    8
+ 7 ☐

Spatial Thinking

Add the dots on the dominoes.
What is the sum?

3.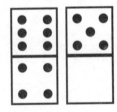

(A) 17

(B) 15

(C) 13

(D) 11

Algebra

Find the missing number.

4. $8 + \_\_\_ + 7 = 19$

(A) 2

(B) 3

(C) 4

(D) 5

Name _____

Word Problems with Three Addends

Sally has some fruit.
She has 3 apples, 5 bananas, and 5 pears.
How many pieces of fruit does she have in all?

 + +

Way 1: First, add the and . Complete the number sentence.

3 + _____ = _____

      ⟋   ◯ and ⟋

Next, add the .

8 + _____ = _____

◯ and ⟋   ⟋   ◯, ⟋, and ◯

· ·

 + +

Way 2: First, add the and ◯. Complete the number sentence.

5 + _____ = _____

⟋   ◯   ⟋ and ◯

Next, add the .

_____ + _____ = _____

⟋ and ◯   ◯   ⟋, ◯, and ◯

Word Problems with Three Addends

Write a number sentence. Find the best way to group the addends.

1. There are some books on the shelf.
There are 3 red books,
3 brown books, and 6 blue books.
How many books are there in all?

____ ◯ ____ ◯ ____ = ____ ____ books

----

2. Hal has some beads.
He has 7 green beads,
4 purple beads, and 6 yellow beads.
How many beads does he have in all?

____ ◯ ____ ◯ ____ = ____ ____ beads

Algebra

3. Terry sees 12 flowers.
He sees 7 roses, 3 tulips,
and some daisies.
How many daisies does he see?

$7 + 3 +$ ____ $= 12$ ____ daisies

Making 10 to Subtract

Making a 10 can help you subtract.
Subtract 14 − 6.

14 altogether

Subtract 4.

There are 10 left.

Subtract 2 more.

You subtracted 6 altogether.

There are 8 left.

$$14 - 6 = \underline{8}$$

Make a 10.
Cross out the counters to help you subtract.
Complete the subtraction fact.

1. 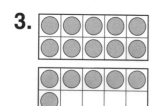 $11 - 5 = \underline{6}$

2. $14 - 5 = \underline{}$

3. $16 - 7 = \underline{}$

4. $15 - 9 = \underline{}$

Making 10 to Subtract

Make a 10 to subtract.
Complete the subtraction fact.

1.

$11 - 8 =$ _____

2.

$14 - 5 =$ _____

3.

$15 - 7 =$ _____

4.

$18 - 9 =$ _____

Reasoning

5. Which subtraction fact does this picture show?

Ⓐ $17 - 8 = 9$

Ⓑ $16 - 10 = 6$

Ⓒ $16 - 9 = 7$

Ⓓ $16 - 8 = 8$

More with Making 10 to Subtract

Here are some different ways to make 10.

There are 12 pears on a tree.
4 pears fall off.
How many pears are left?

Use a counter for each pear.

Cross out 2 counters to make a 10.

Cross out 2 more.

$2 + 2 = 4$

$12 - 4 = 8$

So, 8 pears are left.

Cross out counters to help you subtract.
Write a subtraction sentence.

1. Maria buys 13 tubes of paint.
   She uses 7 tubes of paint.
   How many tubes does
   she have left?

   ____ – ____ = ____

2. Max has 16 buttons on his shirt.
   8 buttons fall off.
   How many buttons are left on his shirt?

   ____ – ____ = ____

More with Making 10 to Subtract

Make a 10 to solve.
Write a subtraction sentence.

1. Nick has 13 sports cards.
   He loses 4 cards.
   How many sports cards
   does Nick have left?

   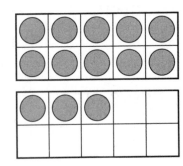

   _____ – _____ = _____

2. Jay picks 11 flowers.
   He gives 8 to his grandmother.
   How many flowers
   does Jay have left?

   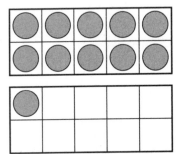

   _____ – _____ = _____

Algebra

3. Anita has 18 beads.
   She uses 9 beads to
   make a necklace.
   How many beads does
   Anita have left?
   Which subtraction sentence
   tells about the story?

   Ⓐ $19 - 9 = 10$ Ⓒ $18 - 8 = 10$

   Ⓑ $18 - 10 = 8$ Ⓓ $18 - 9 = 9$

Using Related Facts

These two facts are related.

The addition sentence and the subtraction sentence have the same 3 numbers.

$9 + 3 = 12$

$12 - 3 = 9$

The sum of the addition sentence is the first number in the subtraction sentence.

Add. Then write a related subtraction fact.

1.

$8 + 4 = \underline{12}$

$\underline{12} - \underline{4} = \underline{8}$

2.

$7 + 6 = \underline{13}$

$\underline{13} - \underline{6} = \underline{}$

3.

$9 + 2 = \underline{}$

$\underline{} - 9 = \underline{}$

4.

$8 + 5 = \underline{}$

$\underline{} - 8 = \underline{}$

5.

$8 + 6 = \underline{}$

$\underline{} - 8 = \underline{}$

6.

$8 + 7 = \underline{}$

$\underline{} - 8 = \underline{}$

Using Related Facts

Write an addition fact and
a related subtraction fact.

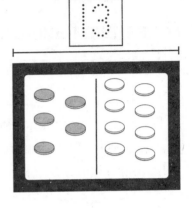

1. ___5___ + ___8___ = ___13___

___13___ – ___8___ = ___5___

2. _____ + _____ = _____

_____ – _____ = _____

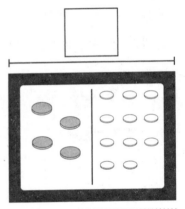

....

Reasoning

Solve the problem.

3. Abby's dad wrote this
addition sentence on
a piece of paper.

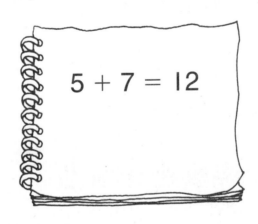

$5 + 7 = 12$

Which subtraction sentence
is related?

Ⓐ $7 + 5 = 12$

Ⓑ $12 - 7 = 5$

Ⓒ $12 - 9 = 3$

Ⓓ $7 - 5 = 2$

Fact Families

This is a fact family.

$8 + 4 = 12$

$4 + 8 = 12$

Each number sentence has the same 3 numbers.

$12 - 8 = 4$

$12 - 4 = 8$

Complete each fact family. Use counters to help you.

1. | 6 | 11 | 5 |

$6 + 5 =$ ____

$5 + \underline{6} = 11$

$11 - 5 = \underline{6}$

$11 - \underline{6} = 5$

2. | 9 | 5 | 14 |

$9 + 5 =$ ____

$5 + \underline{\hphantom{xx}} = 14$

$14 - 5 =$ ____

$14 - \underline{\hphantom{xx}} = 5$

3. | 7 | 6 | 13 |

$7 + 6 =$ ____

$6 + \underline{\hphantom{xx}} = 13$

$13 - 6 =$ ____

$13 - \underline{\hphantom{xx}} = 6$

R 6·4

Fact Families

Write the fact family for the model.

1.

$$\boxed{15}$$

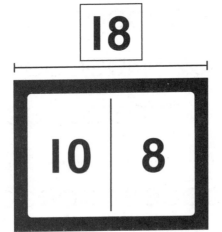

| 8 | 7 |

$$\underline{\;7\;} + \underline{\;8\;} = \underline{\;15\;}$$

$$\underline{\;8\;} + \underline{\;7\;} = \underline{\quad}$$

$$\underline{\;15\;} - \underline{\;8\;} = \underline{\quad}$$

$$\underline{\;15\;} - \underline{\quad} = \underline{\quad}$$

2.

$$\boxed{18}$$

| 10 | 8 |

$$\underline{\quad} + \underline{\quad} = \underline{\quad}$$

$$\underline{\quad} + \underline{\quad} = \underline{\quad}$$

$$\underline{\quad} - \underline{\quad} = \underline{\quad}$$

$$\underline{\quad} - \underline{\quad} = \underline{\quad}$$

Reasoning

Solve the problem.

3. Which related facts
describe this picture?

Ⓐ $4 + 11 = 15,\ 15 - 4 = 11$

Ⓑ $11 - 4 = 7,\ 7 + 4 = 11$

Ⓒ $3 + 7 = 10,\ 10 - 3 = 7$

Ⓓ $7 - 4 = 3,\ 7 - 3 = 4$

Name _____

Using Addition to Subtract

$$6 + 5 = 11$$

$$11 - 5 = \underline{6}$$

> You can use an addition fact to help you write a subtraction fact with the same numbers.

Add. Then use the addition fact to help you subtract.
Use cubes if you like.

1.

$$4 + 9 = \underline{13}$$

$$13 - 9 = \underline{4}$$

2.

$$8 + 7 = \underline{}$$

$$15 - 7 = \underline{}$$

3.

$$7 + 4 = \underline{}$$

$$11 - 4 = \underline{}$$

4.

$$6 + 7 = \underline{}$$

$$13 - 7 = \underline{}$$

R 6·5

Name _____

Using Addition to Subtract

Complete the model.
Then complete the number sentences.

1.

$18 - 8 =$ __10__

$8 +$ _____ $= 18$

2.

$15 - 6 =$ _____

$6 +$ _____ $= 15$

Algebra

3. Which addition fact will help you solve $14 - 9$?

Ⓐ $5 + 14 = 19$

Ⓑ $5 + 9 = 14$

Ⓒ $4 + 9 = 13$

Ⓓ $5 + 7 = 12$

Algebra

4. Draw the missing shape. Then explain how you know.

If ⬡ + ◯ = △

Then △ − ⬡ = ☐

Explain: _____

_____

_____

Subtraction Facts

There are many ways to learn and remember subtraction facts.
One way is to think about a related addition fact.

$12 - 8 = ?$

Think: What plus 8
equals 12?
$? + 8 = 12$

Then you can use a number line to help you add.

By using the line,
I know that
$8 + 4 = 12$

Complete the addition fact. Then solve the subtraction fact.
Use the number line to help you.

1.

$$\begin{array}{r} 5 \\ + 6 \\ \hline \end{array} \qquad \begin{array}{r} 11 \\ - 5 \\ \hline \end{array}$$

2.

$$\begin{array}{r} 9 \\ + \\ \hline 16 \end{array} \qquad \begin{array}{r} 16 \\ - 9 \\ \hline \end{array}$$

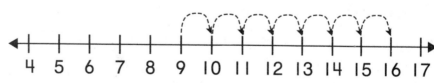

Subtraction Facts

Complete the addition fact.
Then solve the subtraction fact.

1. $16 - 7 = \boxed{}$

$7 + \boxed{} = 16$

2. $14 - 6 = \boxed{}$

$6 + \boxed{} = 14$

Subtract.

3. $\begin{array}{r} 17 \\ -\ 8 \\ \hline \boxed{} \end{array}$

4. $\begin{array}{r} 15 \\ -\ 9 \\ \hline \boxed{} \end{array}$

5. $\begin{array}{r} 14 \\ -\ 6 \\ \hline \boxed{} \end{array}$

6. $\begin{array}{r} 13 \\ -\ 7 \\ \hline \boxed{} \end{array}$

Reasonableness

7. Can the addition fact help you
solve the subtraction problem?

$9 + 9 = 18$
$18 - 9 = ?$

Circle **yes** or **no**.

yes   **no**

Journal

8. Solve $15 - 9$.

Use words, pictures, or numbers
to show how you solved it.

Problem Solving: Draw a Picture and Write a Number Sentence

You can write a number sentence to solve problems.

Avi played 2 games of basketball.
He scored 8 points in the first game.
He scored 6 points in the second game.
How many points did Avi score in all?

You can draw a picture to help you solve the problem.
Then you can write a number sentence.

____8____ + ____6____ = ____14____

Complete the model.
Then write a number sentence.

1. Gina has 9 books.
   She buys 4 more books.
   How many books
   does Gina have now?

_____ (+) _____ = __13__

2. Metta sees 15 frogs.
   7 frogs hop away.
   How many frogs
   are left?

_____ ◯ _____ = _____

Problem Solving: Draw a Picture and Write a Number Sentence

Write a number sentence to solve.
Draw a picture to check your answer.

1. Helen made invitations for her party.
   She made 7 invitations on Monday.
   She made 6 invitations on Tuesday.
   How many invitations
   did Helen make in all?

   _____ ◯ _____ = _____ invitations

2. Joe started at the bottom
   of the stairs.
   He hopped up 9 stairs.
   Then he hopped down 3 stairs.
   How many stairs is Joe
   from the bottom?

   _____ ◯ _____ = _____ stairs

Reasoning

3. Which number sentence
   tells how many apples in all?

   Ⓐ 8 − 7 = 1
   Ⓑ 8 − 1 = 7
   Ⓒ 7 + 1 = 8
   Ⓓ 7 + 8 = 15

Making Numbers 11 to 19

Write each number as 10 and some left over.

This shows 10.

This shows 4 left over.

14 is __10__   and   __4__ .

1.

17 is __10__   and   __7__ .

2.

16 is _____   and   __6__ .

3.

15 is _____   and   _____ .

4.

18 is _____   and   _____ .

R 7·1

Making Numbers 11 to 19

Write each number as 10 and some ones.

1. | twelve | 12 is __10__ and __2__.

2. | eighteen | 18 is _____ and _____.

3. | fourteen | 14 is _____ and _____.

4. | eleven | 11 is _____ and _____.

5. | seventeen | 17 is _____ and _____.

6. | nineteen | 19 is _____ and _____.

7. | sixteen | 16 is _____ and _____.

Algebra

8. Which is the
   missing number?

   13 is 10 and _____.

   Ⓐ 1
   Ⓑ 2
   Ⓒ 3
   Ⓓ 10

9. Which is the
   missing number?

   15 is _____ and 5.

   Ⓐ 10
   Ⓑ 5
   Ⓒ 3
   Ⓓ 1

Name _____

Using Numbers 11 to 19

This shows 12.

Count 10, 11, 12.

This shows **2 more** than 12.

Count 10, 11, 12, 13, 14.
2 more than 12 is 14.

This shows 13.

Count 10, 11, 12, 13.

This shows **2 fewer** than 13.

Count 10, 11.
2 fewer than 13 is 11.

Write the numbers.

1.

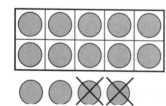

2 more than 13 is ___15___.

2.

1 fewer than 13 is _____.

3.

2 fewer than 14 is _____.

4.

1 more than 10 is _____.

Name _____

Using Numbers 11 to 19

Write the numbers.

1. twelve _____   1 more _____   1 fewer _____

2. seventeen _____   2 more _____   2 fewer _____

3. fifteen _____   2 more _____   2 fewer _____

4. seventeen _____   1 more _____   1 fewer _____

5. thirteen _____   2 more _____   2 fewer _____

Number Sense

6. Jeff has 16 checkers.
   His friend gives him
   2 more checkers.
   Which number tells how
   many checkers he has now?

   Ⓐ   14
   Ⓑ   15
   Ⓒ   17
   Ⓓ   18

Reasonableness

7. There are 12 birds in
   the tree.
   1 bird flies away.
   Which tells how many
   birds are left in the tree?

   Ⓐ   less than 10
   Ⓑ   between 10 and 12
   Ⓒ   between 12 and 15
   Ⓓ   more than 12

Counting by 10s

 stands for one group of ten.

10,	20,	30,	40,	50,
ten,	twenty,	thirty,	forty,	fifty,
60,	70,	80,	90,	
sixty,	seventy,	eighty,	ninety	

_____ groups of ten

40   forty

Count by 10s. Then write the numbers.

1.

_____5_____ groups of ten

fifty

2.

_____ groups of ten

_____ _____

3.

_____ groups of ten

_____ _____

Counting by 10s

10, ten,	20, twenty,	30, thirty,	40, forty,	50, fifty,
60, sixty,	70, seventy,	80, eighty,	90, ninety	

Count by tens. Then write the numbers.

1.

__4__ tens = __40__

forty

2.

_____ tens = _____

_____

3.

_____ tens = _____

_____

Journal

4. Laura wants to show 70 in tens.
How many tens will she draw?
How do you know?

_____

_____

Counting to 120

Use the number chart.

1	2	3	4	5	6	7	8	9	10
11	12	13	14	15	16	17	18	19	20
21	22	23	24	25	26	27	28	29	30
31	32	33	34	35	36	37	38	39	40
41	42	43	44	45	46	47	48	49	50
51	52	53	54	55	56	57	58	59	60
61	62	63	64	65	66	67	68	69	70
71	72	73	74	75	76	77	78	79	80
81	82	83	84	85	86	87	88	89	90
91	92	93	94	95	96	97	98	99	100
101	102	103	104	105	106	107	108	109	110
111	112	113	114	115	116	117	118	119	120

Start at 103.
Then count forward by 1s.

103, <u>104</u>, <u>105</u>

Start at 115.
Then count forward by 1s.

115, <u>116</u>, <u>117</u>

Count forward by 1s.
Write the numbers.

1. 105 _____, _____, _____, _____, _____

2. 111 _____, _____, _____, _____, _____

3. 98 _____, _____, _____, _____, _____

Counting to 120

Count forward by 1s.

1. 104, _____, _____, _____, _____, _____

2. 113, _____, _____, _____, _____, _____

3. 97, _____, _____, _____, _____, _____

4. 111, _____, _____, _____, _____, _____

Number Sense

5. The school lockers show the numbers in order.

Write the missing number.

_____

Using Counting by 10s

Count to find how many.

Count by 10,
or add 10 to the
last number.

_10_, _20_, _30_, _40_

add 10 add 10 add 10

There are __40__ pencils.

---

1. Count by 10s.

_10_, _____, _____, _____, _____, _____

---

2. Count by 10s.

_____, _____, _____, _____, _____

---

3. Count by 10s.

_____, _____, _____, _____, _____, _____

Using Counting by 10s

Use the pictures to count by 10s.

1. How many pencils are there?
Count by 10s.

__10__ , _____ , _____ , _____ , _____ , _____

2. How many cans are there?
Count by 10s.

_____ , _____ , _____ , _____ , _____

3. How many balls are there?
Count by 10s.

_____ , _____ , _____ , _____ , _____ , _____ , _____

Algebra

4. Look for a pattern.
Find the missing number.

30, 40, 50, 60, 70, 80, _____

Ⓐ 20 Ⓒ 70
Ⓑ 50 Ⓓ 90

Number Sense

5. Cal has 8 bags.
He puts 10 marbles in each bag. How many marbles does Cal have in all?

Ⓐ 40 Ⓒ 70
Ⓑ 50 Ⓓ 80

Problem Solving:
Look for a Pattern

The children need mittens.
Each child has two hands.
How many mittens are needed for all of the children?

You need to find how many hands the children
have altogether.

Make a table to show a pattern.
Write the numbers.

Count the children by 1s.
Count the mittens by 2s.

Number of Children	1	2		
Number of Mittens	2	4		

___8___ mittens will be needed for all of the children.
Does your answer make sense?

Find the pattern. Write the numbers.

1. There are 4 boxes.
   Each box has 10 crayons.
   How many crayons are
   there in all?

Number of Boxes	1	2		
Number of Crayons	10			

   There are _____ crayons in all.

Problem Solving:
Look for a Pattern

Find the pattern.
Write the numbers.

1. There are 6 vase.
  Each vase has 10 flowers.
  How many wings are there in all?

Number of Vase	1					
Number of Flowers	10					

2. There are 5 bicycles.
  Each bicycle has 2 wheels.
  How many wheels are there in all?

Number of Tricycles					
Number of Wheels					

Reasoning

3. There are 7 boxes.
  Each box has 10 balls in it.
  How many balls are there in all?

Ⓐ 3
Ⓑ 7
Ⓒ 10
Ⓓ 70

Name _____

Counting with Groups of 10 and Leftovers

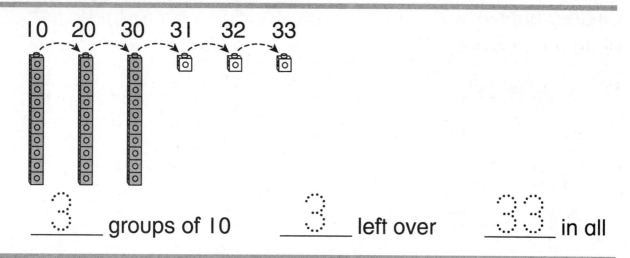

3 groups of 10   **3** left over   **33** in all

Use counters to show the snap cubes.
Make groups of 10.
Then write the numbers.

1. 10 20 21 22 23 24 25 26 27

   2 groups of ten

   7 left over

   _____ in all

2.

_____ groups of ten

_____ left over

_____ in all

Counting with Groups of 10 and Leftovers

Circle groups of 10.
Write the numbers.

1.

_____ is _____ groups of 10 and _____ left over.

2.

_____ is _____ groups of 10 and _____ left over.

Journal

3. 10 beads fit on a bracelet.
Ben has 34 beads.
Draw a picture to show
all the bracelets he
can make with his beads.
Then draw the beads
that will be left over.

Numbers Made with Tens

You can count the models to find out how many groups of ten.

1 ten   2 tens   3 tens   4 tens
is 10.   is 20.   is 30.   is 40.

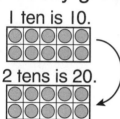

1 ten is 10.

2 tens is 20.

1 ten is 10.

2 tens is 20.

3 tens is 30.

2 tens is _20_.   3 tens is _30_.   4 tens is _40_.

Count the models. Write how many. Then write the number.

1.

_1_ ten is _10_.

_2_ tens is _20_.

_3_ tens is _30_.

_3_ tens is _30_.

2.

____ ten is ____.

____ tens is ____.

____ tens is ____.

____ tens is ____.

_4_ tens is ____.

3.

____ ten is ____.

____ tens is ____.

____ tens is ____.

____ tens is ____.

____ tens is ____.

____ tens is ____.

Numbers Made with Tens

Count by 10s.
Write the numbers.

1.

_____ tens is _____.

2.

_____ tens is _____.

3.

_____ tens is _____.

4.

_____ tens is _____.

Reasonableness

5. What number is shown?

Ⓐ 3
Ⓑ 10
Ⓒ 12
Ⓓ 30

Algebra

6. Nancy has 50 marbles.
30 of the marbles are in
one bag.
The rest are in another bag.
How many marbles are in
the second bag?

Ⓐ 40
Ⓑ 30
Ⓒ 20
Ⓓ 10

Tens and Ones

The chart shows

Tens	Ones

3 tens   4 ones

3 tens is 30.
4 ones is 4.
30 + 4 = 34

> 34 is the same as
> 3 tens and 4 ones.

Count the tens and ones. Then write the numbers.

1.

Tens	Ones

__2__ tens and __4__ ones

__2__ tens is __20__.
__4__ ones is __4__.
__20__ + __4__ = __24__

2.

Tens	Ones

_____ tens and _____ ones

_____ tens is _____.

_____ ones is _____.

_____ + _____ = _____

3.

Tens	Ones

_____ tens and _____ ones

_____ tens is _____.

_____ ones is _____.

_____ + _____ = _____

Tens and Ones

Count the tens and ones. Then write the numbers.

1.

Tens	Ones

⇒

Tens	Ones
4	5

⇒ 45

....

2.

Tens	Ones

⇒

Tens	Ones

⇒ _____

....

3.

Tens	Ones

⇒

Tens	Ones

⇒ _____

....

Estimation

4. About how many cubes
are shown in the picture?

Tens	Ones

70	50	30	10
Ⓐ	Ⓑ	Ⓒ	Ⓓ

Expanded Form

Two-digit numbers are made up of tens and ones.
27 is a two-digit number.

Tens	Ones

2 is in the tens column.
7 is in the ones column.

tens   ones

__2__ tens + __7__ ones = __27__

1.

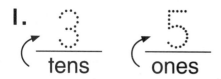
tens   ones

Tens	Ones

__3__ tens + __5__ ones = __35__

....

2.

(_____ (_____
   tens   ones

Tens	Ones

_____ tens + _____ ones = _____

....

3.

(_____ (_____
   ten   one

Tens	Ones

_____ ten + _____ one = _____

Expanded Form

Draw the tens and ones. Then write the numbers.

1.

Tens	Ones

__3__ tens + __6__ ones = 36

__30__ + __6__ = 36

2.

Tens	Ones

_____ tens + _____ ones = _____

_____ + _____ = _____

3.

Tens	Ones

_____ tens + _____ ones = _____

_____ + _____ = _____

Reasoning

4. The number in the tens place is greater than 6.
The digit in the ones place is between 3 and 7.
Which number matches the clues?

Ⓐ 98

Ⓑ 92

Ⓒ 85

Ⓓ 66

Ways to Make Numbers

27

is the
same as

27

__**2**__ tens __**7**__ ones

I ten   I7 ones

$27 = \underline{20} + \underline{7}$

$27 = \underline{10} + \underline{17}$

Use cubes to show a different way
to make the number. Draw the ones.

1.

32

is the
same as

__**3**__ tens __**2**__ ones

__**2**__ tens __**12**__ ones

$32 = \underline{30} + \underline{2}$

$32 = \underline{20} + \underline{12}$

2.

is the
same as

_____ tens _____ ones

_____ tens _____ ones

$43 = \underline{\quad} + \underline{\quad}$

$43 = \underline{\quad} + \underline{\quad}$

Name _____

Practice
8-5

Ways to Make Numbers

Use cubes. Show a different way to make the number.

1.

Tens	Ones

37 = 30 + 7

Break apart a ten into 10 ones.

37 = __20__ + __17__

2.

Tens	Ones

24 = 10 + 14

Make a ten with 10 ones.

24 = _____ + _____

3.

Tens	Ones

62 = 60 + 2

Break apart a ten into 10 ones.

62 = _____ + _____

Number Sense

4. On Mario's workmat, there are 4 tens and 8 ones. Which is another way to show this same number?

Ⓐ 6 tens and 6 ones Ⓒ 3 tens and 18 ones

Ⓑ 3 tens and 9 ones Ⓓ 1 ten and 28 ones

Name _____

Problem Solving:
Make an Organized List

How many ways can you
show 18 with tens and ones?

Tens	Ones
1	8
0	18

How many tens are in 18? ___1___

How many ones are left over? ___8___

Break apart a ten into 10 ones.

How many ones are there? ___18___

Make a list to show the ways.

1. Olivia wants to show 25
   with tens and ones.
   Make a list to show the ways.

Tens	Ones
2	5

Reasonableness

2. Penny says there are 4 ways to make 26.
   Is she correct?

Yes   No

Problem Solving:
Make an Organized List

Use cubes and make a list to solve.

1. Kelly shows all the ways to make 49 as tens and ones. What ways does she show?

Tens	Ones

2. Marc wants to show 34 as tens and ones. What are all the ways he can show?

Tens	Ones

Reasoning

3. Hector's list shows ways to make 52, but he forgot one way. Which numbers are missing from his list?

Tens	Ones
5	2
?	?
3	22
2	32
1	42
0	52

Ⓐ 5 and 12

Ⓑ 4 and 12

Ⓒ 4 and 22

Ⓓ 3 and 12

I More, I Less;
I0 More, I0 Less

34 take away 10 is 24.

10 less than 34 is __24__.

34 and 10 more is 44.

10 more than 34 is __44__.

Use cubes. Write the numbers.

I.

23 take away I is __22__.

I less than 23 is _____.

23 and I more is __24__.

I more than 23 is _____.

- -

2.

I less than 45 is _____.

I more than 45 is _____.

3.

10 less than 68 is _____.

10 more than 68 is _____.

1 More, 1 Less;
10 More, 10 Less

Use cubes. Write the numbers.

1. |72|

I more than 72 is 73.

I less than _____ is _____.

10 more than _____ is _____.

10 less than _____ is _____.

2. |26|

I more than _____ is _____.

I less than _____ is _____.

10 more than _____ is _____.

10 less than _____ is _____.

3. |70|

I more than _____ is _____.

I less than _____ is _____.

10 more than _____ is _____.

10 less than _____ is _____.

4. |14|

I more than _____ is _____.

I less than _____ is _____.

10 more than _____ is _____.

10 less than _____ is _____.

Reasoning

5. Tom is thinking of a number. His number is 10 more than 45. Which number is he thinking of?

   Ⓐ   35

   Ⓑ   44

   Ⓒ   46

   Ⓓ   55

6. Shay is thinking of a number. Her number is 1 less than 87. Which number is she thinking of?

   Ⓐ   97

   Ⓑ   88

   Ⓒ   86

   Ⓓ   77

Making Numbers on a Hundred Chart

1	2	3
11	12→	⑬
21	22	23

Go right to find 1 more.
1 more than 12 is 13.

1	2	3
⑪←	12	13
21	22	23

Go left to find 1 less.
1 less than 12 is 11.

1	2	3
11	12	13
21	㉒	23

Go down to find 10 more.
10 more than 12 is 22.

1	②	3
11	12	13
21	22	23

Go up to find 10 less.
10 less than 12 is 2.

Write the missing numbers.

21	22	23	24	25	26	27	28	29	30
31	32	33	34	35	36	37	38	39	40

1. 1 more than 38 is ___39___ .

2. 1 less than 27 is _____ .

3. 10 more than 23 is _____ .

4. 10 less than 35 is _____ .

Making Numbers on a Hundred Chart

Use the hundred chart to help.

1	2	3	4	5	6	7	8	9	10
11	12	13	14	15	16	17	18	19	20
21	22	23	24	25	26	27	28	29	30
31	32	33	34	35	36	37	38	39	40
41	42	43	44	45	46	47	48	49	50
51	52	53	54	55	56	57	58	59	60
61	62	63	64	65	66	67	68	69	70
71	72	73	74	75	76	77	78	79	80
81	82	83	84	85	86	87	88	89	90
91	92	93	94	95	96	97	98	99	100

1.

1 more than 77 is _____.

1 less than 77 is _____.

10 more than 77 is _____.

10 less than 77 is _____.

2.

1 more than 82 is _____.

1 less than 82 is _____.

10 more than 82 is _____.

10 less than 82 is _____.

3.

1 more than 73 is _____.

1 less than 73 is _____.

10 more than 73 is _____.

10 less than 73 is _____.

4.

1 more than 90 is _____.

1 less than 90 is _____.

10 more than 90 is _____.

10 less than 90 is _____.

Reasoning

5. Sara has 10 more freckles than Tim.
Tim has 1 less freckle than Hank.
Hank has 65 freckles.
How many freckles does Sara have?

76	74	66	55
Ⓐ	Ⓑ	Ⓒ	Ⓓ

Using Models to Compare Numbers

Compare these numbers. First compare the tens.

49 **is greater than** 35.

Compare these numbers.
If the tens are the same, compare the ones.

24 **is less than** 25.

Use cubes to show the numbers. Write **greater than** or **less than** to compare the numbers

1. 40 is **less than** 50.   **2.** 44 is _____ 42.

3. 37 is _____ 34.   **4.** 62 is _____ 63.

Name _____

Using Models to Compare Numbers

Write the number of cubes.
Circle **is greater than** or **is less than.**

1.

is greater than

_____   _____

is less than

2.

is greater than

_____   _____

is less than

---

3. Trevor saw 22 monkeys in a picture. He saw 29 birds in the same picture. Did Trevor see more birds or more monkeys?

more _____

4. Kenya has 18 grapes. She has 21 berries. Does Kenya have more grapes or more berries?

more _____

---

5. Laura counted 36 stars. Andy counted more stars than Laura. How many stars could Andy have counted?

Ⓐ   41
Ⓑ   35
Ⓒ   30
Ⓓ   29

6. Reasoning
What number am I?

My tens digit is double my ones digit. I am less than 70 and greater than 60.

_____

Comparing Numbers
with >, <, =

Write >, <, or =.

23 < 33

33 > 23

23 = 23

< means
less than

> means
greater than

= means
equal to

23 is **less than** 33   33 is **greater than** 23   23 is **equal to** 23

Circle **less than, greater than,** or **equal to.**
Write <, >, or =.

1.
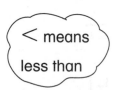

(less than)   greater than   equal to

17 ⊙ 24

2.

less than   greater than   equal to

45 ◯ 32

3.

less than   greater than   equal to

29 ◯ 29

R 9·4

Comparing Numbers with >, <, =

Write >, <, or =.

1. 43 ◯ 52

2. 17 ◯ 16

3. 48 ◯ 58

4. 29 ◯ 86

5. 31 ◯ 31

6. 92 ◯ 57

7. 65 ◯ 37

8. 27 ◯ 27

9. 45 ◯ 50

10. 59 ◯ 41

11. 35 ◯ 53

12. 21 ◯ 12

Number Sense

13. Which sentence is true?

$38 < 30$ $38 > 30$ $38 = 30$ $30 > 38$

Ⓐ   Ⓑ   Ⓒ   Ⓓ

Reasoning

14. Which is equal to 13?

Ⓐ

Ⓑ

Ⓒ

Ⓓ

Name _____

Problem Solving:
Make an Organized List

Kyla picks a number card.
Her number is less than 40.
It is greater than 35.
Which number does she pick?

Make a list to find Kyla's number.

Look at the first clue.
List the numbers on the cards
that are less than 40.

29
32
38

Kyla's number could be 29, 32, or 38.

Look at the second clue.
Circle the numbers on the list
that are greater than 35.
38 is greater than 35.

29
32
38

Kyla's number must be 38.

---

1. Ian picks a number card.
It is less than 60.
Ian says his number when
he counts by 2s.
Which number does Ian pick?

Make a list of the numbers less than 60.
Then circle the number on the list
that Ian says when he counts by 2s.

_____

_____

_____

Ian's number must be _____.

Name _____

Problem Solving:
Make an Organized List

Make a list. Write the color of the motorcycle.

1	2	3	4	5	6	7	8

red	pink	orange	yellow	green	blue	purple	black

1. This motorcycle is between numbers 3 and 6.

Which color could it be?

yellow

_____

This motorcycle is the color of a banana. What color is the motorcycle?

_____

2. This motorcycle is between numbers 1 and 4.

Which color could it be?

_____

_____

This motorcycle is the color of a pumpkin. What color is the motorcycle?

_____

Reasoning

Make a list to find the secret number.

3. I am a number greater than 55.
I am in a square.
What number am I?

Ⓐ 28   Ⓒ 60
Ⓑ 63   Ⓓ 78

/35\ (23) [28]

/52\ (43) [48]

/60\ (63) [78]

Adding Groups of 10

You can use what you know about adding ones
to add groups of 10.

2 ones and 5 ones are 7 ones.   2 tens and 5 tens are 7 tens.

| 2 | + | 5 | = | 7 | | 20 | + | 50 | = | 70 |

Write each number sentence.

1.

$$\underline{3} + \underline{2} = \underline{5}$$ $$\underline{30} + \underline{20} = \underline{50}$$

2.

$$\underline{} + \underline{} = \underline{6}$$ $$\underline{} + \underline{} = \underline{60}$$

3.

$$\underline{} + \underline{} = \underline{}$$ $$\underline{} + \underline{} = \underline{}$$

4.   **5.**

$$\underline{} + \underline{} = \underline{}$$ $$\underline{} + \underline{} = \underline{}$$

Adding Groups of 10

Write numbers to complete each number sentence.

1.

____ tens + ____ tens = ____ tens

____ + ____ = ____

Complete each number sentence.

2. 50 + 20 = ____

3. 30 + 40 = ____

4. 20 + 30 = ____

5. 70 + 20 = ____

6. 60 + 30 = ____

7. 10 + 80 = ____

Number Sense

8. David has 2 books of stamps.
The first book has 50 stamps.
The other book has 30 stamps.
How many stamps does David have in all?

Ⓐ   20

Ⓑ   70

Ⓒ   80

Ⓓ   90

Adding Tens on a Hundred Chart

1	2	3	4	5	6	7	8	9	10
11	12	13	14	15	16	17	18	19	20
21	22	23	24	25	26	27	28	29	30
31	32	33	34	35	36	37	38	39	40
41	42	43	44	45	46	47	48	49	50
51	52	53	54	55	56	57	58	59	60
61	62	63	64	65	66	67	68	69	70
71	72	73	74	75	76	77	78	79	80
81	82	83	84	85	86	87	88	89	90
91	92	93	94	95	96	97	98	99	100

When you add tens on a hundred chart, you count by 10s. The ones digit in each number is the same as the ones digit in the number you started from.

The tens digit of each number is one more than the tens digit of the number before it.

Use the hundred chart to add tens to 16.

1.
$$16$$
$$+ 10$$
$$26$$

2.
$$16$$
$$+ 20$$

3.
$$16$$
$$+ 30$$

4.
$$16$$
$$+ 40$$

5. What number did you count by on the hundred chart to find the answers? _____

Algebra

6. Fill in the missing digits to complete the pattern.

5_____, 62, _____2, _____2

Adding Tens on a Hundred Chart

1	2	3	4	5	6	7	8	9	10
11	12	13	14	15	16	17	18	19	20
21	22	23	24	25	26	27	28	29	30
31	32	33	34	35	36	37	38	39	40
41	42	43	44	45	46	47	48	49	50
51	52	53	54	55	56	57	58	59	60
61	62	63	64	65	66	67	68	69	70
71	72	73	74	75	76	77	78	79	80
81	82	83	84	85	86	87	88	89	90
91	92	93	94	95	96	97	98	99	100

Use the hundred chart to add tens.

1. $24 + 30 =$ _____ $56 + 20 =$ _____ $13 + 70 =$ _____

2. $11 + 80 =$ _____ $67 + 10 =$ _____ $39 + 40 =$ _____

Algebra

3. Which number sentence is equal
to $24 + 10$?

Ⓐ $14 + 10$

Ⓑ $14 + 20$

Ⓒ $24 + 20$

Ⓓ $34 + 10$

Adding Tens to Two-Digit Numbers

You can count on by tens to add.

3 tens

28 + 30 is 28 + 3 tens

28, __38__ __48__, __58__

28 + 30 = 58

Solve each number sentence.

1.

10 10 10 10 10

31, __41__, __51__, __61__, __71__, __81__

31 + 50 is 31 + __5__ tens

31 + 50 = __81__

2.

52, _____ _____

52 + 20 is 52 + _____ tens

52 + 20 = _____

3.

33, _____, _____, _____, _____

33 + 40 is 33 + _____ tens

33 + 40 = _____

Name _____

Adding Tens to Two-Digit Numbers

Write each number sentence.

1. Think

36

$$\underline{36} + \underline{20} = \underline{56}$$

2. Think

54

_____ + _____ = _____

3. Think

63

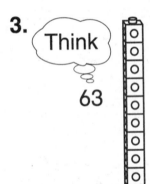

_____ + _____ = _____

4. Think

47

_____ + _____ = _____

Number Sense

5. Will has 24 crayons.
He gets 4 more boxes of crayons.
Each box has 10 crayons.
How many crayons does Will have now?

64	54	44	34
Ⓐ	Ⓑ	Ⓒ	Ⓓ

Mental Math

Use mental math to add these two-digit numbers: 15 + 20.
You just need to add the tens.
Only the tens digit will change.

15 + **20** = <u>3</u>5

Add using mental math. Complete the addition sentence.

1. 32 + 20

<u>32</u> + 20 = <u>52</u>

2. 28 + 40

_____ + 40 = _____

3. 33 + 50

_____ + 50 = _____

4. 47 + 30

_____ + 30 = _____

5. Add using mental math. Use models if needed.

56 + 30 = _____

Name _____

Mental Math

Add using mental math. Use models if you need to.

1. **and 30**

_41_ + _30_ = _71_

2. **and 20**

_____ + _____ = _____

3. 71 + 20 = _____

4. 65 + 30 = _____

5. 40 + 23 = _____

6. 60 + 24 = _____

7. Tanner has 50 star stickers. She has 17 rainbow stickers. How many stickers does Tanner have in all?

47   50   57   67
Ⓐ   Ⓑ   Ⓒ   Ⓓ

8. Darrin has 27 basketball stickers. He has 30 football stickers. How many stickers does Darrin have in all?

63   27   57   68
Ⓐ   Ⓑ   Ⓒ   Ⓓ

9. Algebra Write the missing numbers that make these number sentences true.

40 + 50 = 60 + _____   _____ = 89 + 10

Adding to a Two-Digit Number

Add 26 and 5.

Show 26.   Add 5.

Regroup 10 ones as 1 ten.

Tens	Ones

Tens	Ones

Tens	Ones

Tens	Ones

$26 + 5 = \underline{31}$

Find the sum.

1. Add 16 and 7.

Show 16.   Add 7.   Regroup.   Find the sum.

Tens	Ones

Tens	Ones

Tens	Ones

Tens	Ones

$16 + 7 = \underline{23}$

2. Add 28 and 5.

Show 28.   Add 5.   Regroup.   Find the sum.

Tens	Ones

Tens	Ones

Tens	Ones

Tens	Ones

$28 + 5 = \underline{}$

Adding to a Two-Digit Number

Write the sum.

Find the sum.	**Do you need to regroup?**

1. 27 + 6 = __33__   yes   no

2. 43 + 5 = _____   yes   no

3. 34 + 8 = _____   yes   no

4. 17 + 4 = _____   yes   no

5. 56 + 3 = _____   yes   no

6. 93 + 2 = _____   yes   no

7. 87 + 7 = _____   yes   no

8. 68 + 5 = _____   yes   no

9. 36 + 3 = _____   yes   no

10. Journal There are 24 counters.
How many counters could you add
without having to regroup? Why?

_____

_____

_____

Problem Solving: Draw a Picture and Write a Number Sentence

Add multiples of ten to two-digit numbers. Look for clue words to help you decide.

Lois has 16 counters.
She gets 10 more counters.
How many counters does Lois have in all?

> **In all** tells you that you need to add.

Draw a picture. 26

Write a number sentence.

16 ⊕ 10 = 26

Tens	Ones
☐	
①	⑥
+ 1	0
②	6

Lois has 26 counters.

Circle the words that tell you to add.
Draw a picture and write a number sentence to solve.
Use your workmat to help.

1. Carlos has 17 counters.
   He gets 20 more counters.
   How many counters does he have in all?

37

____ + ____ = ____

____ counters

Problem Solving: Draw a Picture and Write a Number Sentence

Write a number sentence.
Then solve the problem.

1. Jan has 14 stamps.
She gets 30 more stamps.
How many stamps does she have now?

____ ◯ ____ = ____

____ stamps

2. Max has 19 cherries.
His brother gives him 10 more cherries.
How many cherries does Max have now?

____ ◯ ____ = ____

____ cherries

Reasoning

3. Bill says that he can add 23 and 40 without regrouping.
Is Bill correct? How do you know?

_____

_____

_____

_____

Subtracting Groups of 10

You can use what you know about subtracting ones to subtract groups of ten.

$7 - 2 = 5$

$70 - 20 = ?$

Show 7 tens. Take away 2 tens.
Count the tens left over.
Then complete the number sentence.

7 tens − __2__ tens = 5 tens, so 70 − 20 = __50__.

Write the numbers to complete each subtraction sentence.

1. ____ tens − ____ tens = ____ ten

____ − ____ = ____

2. ____ tens − ____ tens = ____ tens

____ − ____ = ____

3. ____ tens − ____ tens = ____ tens

____ − ____ = ____

Number Sense

4. Simon has 7 tens.
Can he take away 9 tens?
Circle Yes or No.

Yes   No

Subtracting Groups of 10

Write the numbers to complete each number sentence.

1. _____ tens − _____ ten = _____ tens

   _____ − _____ = _____

2. _____ tens − _____ tens = _____ ten

   _____ − _____ = _____

3. _____ tens − _____ tens = _____ ten

   _____ − _____ = _____

Algebra

4. Cross out some tens in the picture.
   Then fill in the number sentence.

   5 tens − _____ tens = 3 tens

   50 − _____ = 30

Subtracting Tens on a Hundred Chart

1	2	3	4	5	6	7	8	9	10
11	12	13	14	15	16	17	18	19	20
21	22	23	24	25	26	27	28	29	30
31	32	33	34	35	36	37	38	39	40
41	42	43	44	45	46	47	48	49	50
51	52	53	54	55	56	57	58	59	60
61	62	63	64	65	66	67	68	69	70
71	72	73	74	75	76	77	78	79	80
81	82	83	84	85	86	87	88	89	90
91	92	93	94	95	96	97	98	99	100

To subtract by tens, you can count back by 10s on a hundred chart. Move up a row for each ten you subtract. All of the numbers will end in the same number.

$40 - 30 =$ _____

Count back by tens on the hundred chart to subtract.

1.
$$\begin{array}{r} 80 \\ -60 \\ \hline \end{array}$$
20

2.
$$\begin{array}{r} 50 \\ -10 \\ \hline \end{array}$$

3.
$$\begin{array}{r} 90 \\ -70 \\ \hline \end{array}$$

4.
$$\begin{array}{r} 70 \\ -40 \\ \hline \end{array}$$

5. What number do you count back by on
the hundred chart to find the answers? _____

Algebra

6. Fill in the missing digits to complete the pattern.

8_____, 70, _____0, _____0

Subtracting Tens on a Hundred Chart

1	2	3	4	5	6	7	8	9	10
11	12	13	14	15	16	17	18	19	20
21	22	23	24	25	26	27	28	29	30
31	32	33	34	35	36	37	38	39	40
41	42	43	44	45	46	47	48	49	50
51	52	53	54	55	56	57	58	59	60
61	62	63	64	65	66	67	68	69	70
71	72	73	74	75	76	77	78	79	80
81	82	83	84	85	86	87	88	89	90
91	92	93	94	95	96	97	98	99	100

Use the hundred chart to subtract tens.

I. $80 - 40 =$ _____ $50 - 30 =$ _____ $70 - 60 =$ _____

2. $90 - 10 =$ _____ $30 - 20 =$ _____ $80 - 50 =$ _____

3. $40 - 20 =$ _____ $70 - 50 =$ _____ $60 - 40 =$ _____

Algebra

4. Which number completes the subtraction sentence?

$70 -$ _____ $= 30$

Ⓐ   20

Ⓑ   30

Ⓒ   40

Ⓓ   50

Subtracting Tens from Two-Digit Numbers

You can count back by tens to subtract.

2 tens

10   10

40, __30__ , __20__

40 – 20   is   40 – 2 tens

40 – 20 = __20__

Solve each number sentence.

1.

10

30, __20__

30 – 10   is   30 – __1__ ten

30 – 10 = __20__

2.

10

50, _____, _____, _____

50 – 30   is   50 – _____ tens

50 – 30 = _____

3.

60, _____, _____, _____, _____

60 – 40   is   60 – _____ tens

60 – 40 = _____

Subtracting Tens from Two-Digit Numbers

Cross out the tens. Write the difference.

1.

60 − 20 = _____

2.

40 − 30 = _____

3.

50 − 40 = _____

4.

30 − 10 = _____

Journal

5. Roberto says that 70 − 30 = 30.
Is Roberto correct?
Explain.

_____

_____

Using Mental Math to Subtract Tens

Here are two ways you can find 80 − 20.

1. Count back 2 tens, or 20.

80, _70_, _60_

When you subtract tens, only the tens digit changes.

2. Use cubes to subtract the tens.

80 − 20 = _60_

So, 80 − 20 = _60_.

Count back to subtract tens. Use cubes if needed.

1. 30 − 30 =

30, _20_, _10_, _0_

30 − 30 = _0_

---

2. 80 − 30 = ____

3. 20 − 10 = ____

---

4. 60 − 50 = ____

5. 80 − 70 = ____

---

6. 70 − 40 = ____

7. 40 − 20 = ____

Using Mental Math to Subtract Tens

Subtract. Use mental math or ten-frame cards.

1. 60 − 50 = _____

2. 80 − 40 = _____

3. 40 − 20 = _____

4. 30 − 20 = _____

5. 20 − 10 = _____

6. 50 − 30 = _____

7. 80 − 70 = _____

Ⓐ 70

Ⓑ 50

Ⓒ 30

Ⓓ 10

8. 60 − 40 = _____

Ⓐ 10

Ⓑ 20

Ⓒ 30

Ⓓ 40

9. Use mental math to solve.

A jar holds 50 marbles. Laine is playing with 10 of them.

How many marbles are left in the jar?

Ⓐ 10

Ⓑ 20

Ⓒ 40

Ⓓ 50

10. Number Sense Marco had 90 cards. He gave 50 of them to Susan.

How many cards does he have left?

Ⓐ 80

Ⓑ 60

Ⓒ 50

Ⓓ 40

Problem Solving: Draw a Picture and Write a Number Sentence

Read and Understand

Mr. Yee has 40 pencils.
He gives away 30 pencils.
How many pencils does he have left?

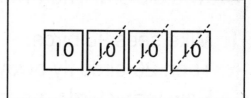

Plan

You can draw a picture and write a number sentence to solve.

Solve

Draw 4 squares for 40 pencils. Cross out 3 squares for 30 pencils.
Count the leftover squares. Then write a number sentence.

$40 - \underline{30} = \underline{10}$, so Mr. Yee has $\underline{10}$ pencils left.

Look Back and Check

You can check if your number sentence matches your picture.

Draw a picture. Then write a number sentence.

1. Alice gathered 60 flowers.
She gives 40 flowers to her friend.
How many flowers does
Alice have left?

_____ − _____ = _____

2. Jake counts 30 ants.
He counts 10 bees.
How many more ants
than bees does he count?

_____ − _____ = _____

Problem Solving: Draw a Picture and Write a Number Sentence

Draw a picture. Then write a number sentence.

1. Mike sees 40 birds.
Then 20 birds fly away.
How many birds are left?

_____ – _____ = _____

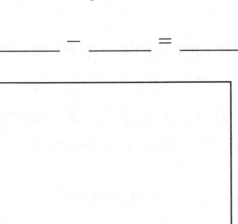

2. Sam has 60 stickers.
She gives away 50 stickers.
How many stickers does
Sam have left?

_____ – _____ = _____

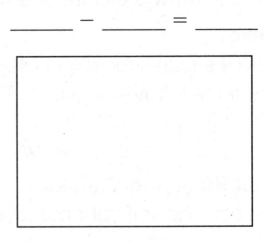

3. Tom drew 70 circles.
Then he drew 40 triangles.
How many more circles than
triangles did he draw?

_____ – _____ = _____

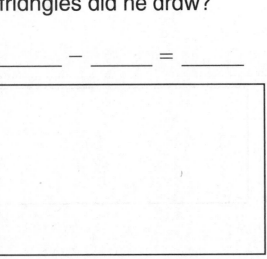

4. A farm has 30 cows and
20 pigs. How many more
cows than pigs does the
farm have?

_____ – _____ = _____

Comparing and Ordering by Length

You can compare and order objects by how long they are.

Line up the objects.

Look to see which
object is longest
and which is shortest.

Then put the objects in order
from longest to shortest.

I. Complete the sentences.

Line A ————————————————

Line B ———————————————

Line C —————————————————

Line _____ is the longest.   Line _____ is the shortest.

Reasoning

2. Use the clues to color the scarves.
The shortest scarf is red.
The green scarf is longer
than the blue scarf.

Comparing and Ordering by Length

Draw lines to match the object with the word that describes it.

I. longest

shortest

2. longest

shortest

Spatial Thinking

3. Grace has the longest scarf.
Which child is Grace?

Ⓐ A

Ⓑ B

Ⓒ C

Ⓓ D

A   B   C   D

Reasoning

4. Use the clues to color the cars.

The shortest car is green.
The yellow car is longer than
the red car.

Indirect Measurement

You can compare two objects that are not together
by using a third object.

The gray triangle is taller than the dotted triangle.
The white triangle is shorter than the dotted triangle.
So, the gray triangle is taller than the white triangle.

1. Circle the striped or gray object that is longer.

Use the white object to help.

2. Circle the dotted or black object that is shorter.

Use the white object to help.

3. Fill in the blanks.

The striped ribbon is _____ than
the gray ribbon.

The _____ ribbon is shorter than
the black ribbon.

Indirect Measurement

Circle the black or white object that is shorter.
Use the gray object to help.

1.

2.

3.

4. Which ribbon answers the riddle?

I am longer than the spotted ribbon.
I am shorter than the gray ribbon.

Ⓐ

Ⓑ

Ⓒ

Ⓓ

Using Units to Estimate and Measure Length

Look at the paper clip.

Look at the string.

Estimate: How many paper clips long is the string?

About _____5_____ paper clips long.

Now measure.

Be sure you put the paper clips right next to each other.

Be sure paper clips are all the same size.

Line up the first paper clip with the edge.

Measure: About _____3_____ paper clips long.
That is close to the estimate.

Estimate. Then measure using paper clips.

I.

	Estimate	Measure
about _____ ⇔		_____ ⇔

2.

	Estimate	Measure
about _____ ⇔		_____ ⇔

3.

	Estimate	Measure
about _____ ⇔		_____ ⇔

Using Units to Estimate and Measure Length

Estimate the length. Then use cubes to measure.

Estimate

Measure

1. about _____   about _____

2. about _____   about _____

Reasoning

3. Which is the best estimate for the length of the stapler?

Ⓐ 6
Ⓑ 7
Ⓒ 14
Ⓓ 17

More Measuring Length

You can compare and order the lengths of 3 objects.
First measure the length of each object. Use cubes to measure.

about __8__ 🧊   about __6__ 🧊   about __7__ 🧊

 __8__ 🧊 is more than __6__ 🧊 and more than __7__ 🧊.
The solid ribbon is the longest.

__6__ 🧊 is less than __8__ 🧊 and less than __7__ 🧊.
The dotted ribbon is the shortest.

Measure the length of each ribbon.
Write which ribbon is the longest and which is the shortest.

Ribbon A

     about __4__ 🧊

Ribbon B

     about _____ 🧊

Ribbon C

     about _____ 🧊

_____ 🧊 is more than _____ 🧊 and more than _____ 🧊.

Ribbon _____ is the longest.

_____ 🧊 is less than _____ 🧊 and less than _____ 🧊.

Ribbon _____ is the shortest.

Name _____

More Measuring Length

Find each object in your classroom.
Measure how long or how tall with cubes.

Measure

1.

how long: about _____ 🎲

2.

how long: about _____ 🎲

3.

how long: about _____ 🎲

---

4. Look at the desk and the bulletin board above.
Circle the longer object.
Draw an X on the shorter object.

---

5. Which shows these objects in
order from shortest to tallest?

tall chair: about 30 🎲
tall book: about 10 🎲
tall basket: about 20 🎲

Ⓐ   chair, book, basket

Ⓑ   basket, chair, book

Ⓒ   chair, basket, book

Ⓓ   book, basket, chair

Problem Solving: Use Reasoning

Look at the marker.
About how many paper clips long is the marker?

Estimate. When you estimate, you make a good guess.

I think the marker is _____ paper clips long.

Then, measure using paper clips.
Line up the paper clips end to end.

The marker is about __5__ paper clips long.

---

1. Use paper clips. Estimate the length.
Then measure to check.

Estimate: about _____ paper clips

Measure: about _____ paper clips

Name _____

Problem Solving: Use Reasoning

Find each object in your classroom.
Use paper clips to estimate and measure.

Object	Estimate	Measure
1. pencil	about _____ ⊂▭⊃	about _____ ⊂▭⊃
2. crayon	about _____ ⊂▭⊃	about _____ ⊂▭⊃

Reasonableness

Circle your answer.

3. Eric has a paintbrush that is about 12 cubes long.
How many paper clips long could it be?

2 ⊂▭⊃   7 ⊂▭⊃   12 ⊂▭⊃

Spatial Thinking

4. Which object would you need the fewest of
to measure how long the eraser is?

Ⓐ

Ⓑ ⊂▭⊃

Ⓒ

Ⓓ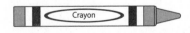
Crayon

Measuring using Different Units

This is I cube.

Cubes can be helpful for measuring shorter objects.

It's easier to say
"A ribbon is 3 cubes long"
than "A ribbon is not as long as a straw."

It's also easier to understand.

This is I straw.

Straws can be helpful for measuring longer objects.

It's easier to say
"A rug is 6 straws long"
than "A rug is 32 cubes long."

It's also easier to understand.

Look at the items below. Decide if you would use cubes or straws to measure. Circle your answer.

I.   **cubes**   **straws**

2.   **cubes**   **straws**

3.   **cubes**   **straws**

Name _____

Measuring Using Different Units

Find each object in your classroom.
Estimate its length.
Then measure using straws.

	Estimate	Measure
I.	about _____ straws	about _____ straws
2.	about _____ straws	about _____ straws
3.	about _____ straws	about _____ straws

Reasonableness

4. Which is the best estimate
for the length of the bicycle?

Ⓐ   about 4 cubes

Ⓑ   about 9 cubes

Ⓒ   about 4 straws

Ⓓ   about 9 straws

Understanding the Hour and Minute Hands

The hour hand
points to the 6.   hour hand __6__

The minute hand
points to the 12.   minute hand __12__

When the minute hand
points to 12, say o'clock.   __6__ o'clock

Write the time shown on each clock.

1.   hour hand __3__

minute hand __12__

__3__ o'clock

2.   hour hand _____

minute hand _____

_____ o'clock

3.   hour hand _____

minute hand _____

_____ o'clock

4.   hour hand _____

minute hand _____

_____ o'clock

Reasoning

Write the times that come next.

5. 4 o'clock   5 o'clock   _____ o'clock

6. 9 o'clock   10 o'clock   _____ o'clock

Understanding the Hour and Minute Hands

Draw an hour hand and a minute hand
to show each time.

1.

7 o'clock

2.

10 o'clock

3.

2 o'clock

4.

1 o'clock

5.

8 o'clock

6.

11 o'clock

Algebra

7. Mark the missing time.

2 o'clock, _____, 4 o'clock

Ⓐ   1 o'clock

Ⓑ   3 o'clock

Ⓒ   5 o'clock

Ⓓ   9 o'clock

8. Mark the missing time.

4 o'clock, _____, 6 o'clock

Ⓐ   10 o'clock

Ⓑ   5 o'clock

Ⓒ   3 o'clock

Ⓓ   2 o'clock

Telling and Writing Time to the Hour

Both clocks show 4 o'clock.

4 tells the hour and...

...00 tells the minutes.

The clocks show the same time.

Draw lines to match the clocks that show the same time.

1.

2.

3.

4.

Telling and Writing Time to the Hour

Draw the hands on each clock face.
Then write the time on the other clock.

1.

12 o'clock

2.

3 o'clock

3.

7 o'clock

4.

10 o'clock

Reasoning

5. Mark the clock that shows the same time as this clock.

Ⓐ 12:00

Ⓑ 7:00

Ⓒ 8:00

Ⓓ 9:00

Telling and Writing Time to the Half Hour

When it is 7:30, the hour hand will be halfway between

_7_ and _8_.

The minute hand

will be on _6_.

The hour hand is shorter than the minute hand.

Complete the sentences.
Then draw the hands on the clock face.

1.

The hour hand will be halfway

between _3_ and _4_.

The minute hand will be on _6_.

2.

The hour hand will be halfway

between _____ and _____.

The minute hand will be on _____.

3.

The hour hand will be halfway

between _____ and _____.

The minute hand will be on _____.

Telling and Writing Time to the Half Hour

Write the time shown on each clock.

1.

2.

3.

4.

Journal

5. Show 3:00 on the first clock.
On the second clock, show the time
30 minutes later.
Is the hour hand still on 3?
Explain.

_____

_____

_____

Problem Solving:
Use Data from a Table

Nature Center Schedule	
Activity	**Time**
🚶 Hike	9:00
🐢 Feed Turtles	10:00
🌸 Pick Flowers	11:00
🐤 Bird Watch	12:00

A schedule tells the time at which activities start.

Look for the activity.

The hike starts at _9:00_.

Look at the time.

At 12:00 we _bird watch_.

Use the schedule to answer the questions. Circle your answer.

1. Which activity comes just before feeding the turtles?

Bird Watch   Hike   Pick Flowers

2. Which activity comes just after picking flowers?

Hike   Feed Turtles   Bird Watch

3. What time does the activity Pick Flowers begin?

9:00   10:00   11:00

4. Which activity starts at 10:00?

Hike   Feed Turtles   Bird Watch

Problem Solving:
Use Data from a Table

Use the schedule to answer the questions.

Time	Activity	
9:00		Art
9:30		T-Ball
10:00		Music
10:30		Puppet Theater
11:00		Swimming

1. Which activity is at 9:00? _____

2. Which activity is just
before Music? _____

3. Which activity is just after
Puppet Theater? _____

Reasoning

4. What time does Music begin?

9:00   9:30   10:00   10:30

Ⓐ   Ⓑ

Using Data from Picture Graphs

Use the graph to answer the questions.

Favorite Seasons						
☀ Summer	☀	☀	☀	☀	☀	☀
🍁 Fall	🍁	🍁	🍁	🍁		
❄ Winter	❄	❄	❄			
🌷 Spring	🌷	🌷	🌷	🌷	🌷	

1. How many children chose winter? _____

2. How many fewer children chose Winter than Spring? _____

3. Which season did 4 children choose? _____

Number Sense

4. How many more children chose summer than spring?

Ⓐ 11

Ⓑ 6

Ⓒ 5

Ⓓ 1

Reasoning

5. How many children voted in all?

Ⓐ 6

Ⓑ 14

Ⓒ 18

Ⓓ 20

Using Data from Picture Graphs

You can use information in picture graphs to answer questions.

Each party hat stands for 1 vote.

10 children voted.

Favorite Party Hat						
Stripes	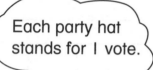					
Polka Dots						

How many children voted for the hat with stripes? ___4___

How many children voted for the hat with polka dots? ___6___

How many more children voted for hats with dots than stripes?

___2___

Favorite Club						
Science						
Art						

1. How many children in all voted for a favorite club? ___11___

2. How many children voted for Science Club? _____

3. How many fewer children voted for Art Club than _____ the Science Club?

4. Which club got more votes?   Science   Art

Name _____

Using Data from Real Graphs

Look at the graph. Circle the correct answers.
Write the number.

1. Is there the same number
   of colored counters?
   yes   no

2. Which color has more?
   gray   black

3. How many counters do
   not have a partner?

   _____

4. Is there the same number of
   colored counters?
   yes   no

5. Which color has more?
   gray   black

6. How many counters do
   not have a partner? _____

Journal

7. Draw black counters
   on the graph
   so there is 1 more
   black counter than gray.

Using Data from Real Graphs

You can use real objects
to make a graph by arranging
the objects in rows and columns.

This is a real-object
graph because the
counters are real
objects.

Circle each pair of counters in the graph.

Is there the same number of colors?   Yes   No

Which color has more?   Black   White

How many counters do not have a partner? ___2___

I. Circle the correct answers. Write the number.

Is there the same number of colors?   Yes   No

Which color has more?   Black   White

How many counters do not have a partner? _____

Name _____

Using Data from Bar Graphs

You can use information in bar graphs to answer questions.

Each shaded square stands for I vote. The shaded squares in a row form a bar.

The least favorite day has the shortest bar.

Favorite Weekend Day

| Saturday | | | | | | | |
| Sunday | | | | | | | |

0   I   2   3   4   5   6   7   8

How many votes did each day get?

Saturday _7_   Sunday _3_

How many more children chose
Saturday than Sunday?   _____ more

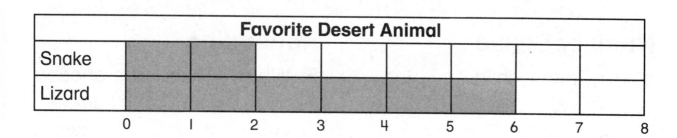

Favorite Desert Animal

| Snake | | | | | | | |
| Lizard | | | | | | | |

0   I   2   3   4   5   6   7   8

I. How many votes did each animal get?

Snake _____ Lizard_____

2. How many more children
chose Lizard than Snake?   _____ more

Name _____

Using Data from Bar Graphs

Use the graph to answer the questions.

1. Mrs. Dunne's class made a graph of their favorite meals. Which meal is the least favorite?

_____

2. How many children voted

for breakfast? _____

3. How many more children voted for

dinner than for lunch? _____

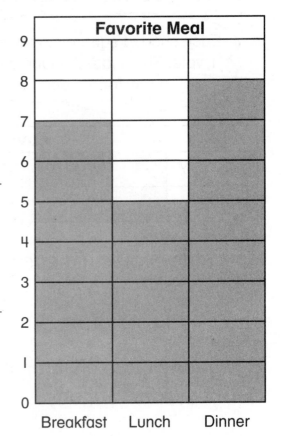

Number Sense

4. How many children voted for lunch?

    (A) 5

    (B) 7

    (C) 8

    (D) 9

Reasoning

5. Which meals were chosen by more than 6 children?

    (A) breakfast and lunch

    (B) breakfast and dinner

    (C) breakfast, lunch, and dinner

    (D) lunch and dinner

Collecting Data
Using Tally Marks

The children made tally marks to show the ways children get to school.

| equals 1

count 5 6 7

|||| equals 5

		Total
Walk	卌 ||	7
School bus	卌 卌	10

count 5   10

---

1. Color some balloons red. Color the rest blue.
Use tally marks to show how many balloons
there are in each color. Write the totals.

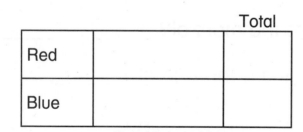

		Total
Red		
Blue		

····························

Use the tally chart to answer the questions.

2. Of which color are there more balloons? _____

3. Of which color are there fewer balloons? _____

4. How many balloons are there altogether? _____

Collecting Data
Using Tally Marks

Make tally marks to show how many flowers
of each kind there are. Then write each total.

Total

1.

Rose			
Tulip			
Daisy			

Use your tally to answer the questions.

2. Which kind of flower is there the most of? _____

3. How many daisies and roses are there in all? _____

Algebra

4. How many more daisies
than tulips are there?

    Ⓐ 2
    Ⓑ 3
    Ⓒ 5
    Ⓓ 7

Reasoning

5. How many roses and
tulips are there in all?

    Ⓐ 15
    Ⓑ 13
    Ⓒ 12
    Ⓓ 3

Making Real Graphs

You can use a tally chart
to make a real graph.

The chart shows Kim has 5 gray cubes
and 3 white cubes.

Kim's Cubes—Tally Chart		
	⊬	5
	⫼	3

How many 🔲 will you put in the graph?   5

How many 🔲 will you put in the graph?   3

I. Use the tally chart to make
a graph with cubes.

Reba's Cubes—Tally Chart		
	⫼⫼	4
	⊬ I	6

2. If you add I gray cube to the graph,
how many gray cubes will there be?   _____ gray cubes

Making Real Graphs

Sarina used cubes to make a picture of a cow.
She used a tally chart to show how many cubes of each color she used in her picture.

1. Use the tally chart to make a graph.

Connecting Cubes Cow – Tally Chart			
■	Black	||||	5
■	Green	||	2
■	Blue	||||		6
■	White	|||	3

Connecting Cubes Cow – Real Graph					
Black					
Green					
Blue					
White					

Number Sense

2. Sarina adds 4 more green cubes to her picture.
How many green cubes are there now?

10	9	7	6
Ⓐ	Ⓑ	Ⓒ	Ⓓ

Making Picture Graphs

You can use a tally chart
to make a picture graph.

Draw a flower for each tally mark.

Favorite Flower	
🌼	IIII I
🌷	III

Favorite Flower					
🌼 Daisy	🌼	🌼	🌼	🌼	🌼
🌷 Tulip	🌷	🌷	🌷		

In how many boxes did you draw a daisy? __5__

In how many boxes did you draw a tulip? __3__

How many more daisies did you draw than tulips? __2__

1. Ask your friends to vote for apple juice or milk as their favorite drink.
   Make a tally chart and a picture graph.

Favorite Drink	
JUICE	
MILK	

Apple Juice					
Milk					

2. How many of your friends voted for apple juice? _____

3. How many more friends voted for Apple Juice than Milk? _____

Name _____

Making Picture Graphs

Favorite Items to Collect	Tally Marks	Totals
🐚 Shells	|||	3
✉ Stamps	ⅢⅠ	6
🪙 Coins	||||	4

1. Use the information in the tally chart.
Draw pictures to make a picture graph.

Favorite Items to Collect						
🐚 Shells						
✉ Stamps						
🪙 Coins						

2. Which item is the least favorite to collect? _____

3. Write the items in order from most favored to least favored.

_____   _____   _____

   most favored   least favored

....

Number Sense

4. How many more people chose
stamps than coins?

10	6	4	2
Ⓐ	Ⓑ	Ⓒ	Ⓓ

Problem Solving:
Make a Graph

Each square that is colored gray equals 1 child's selection.

Name of
Fairy-Tale
Characters

Number of selections

Look at the number of squares colored for the princess.

How many squares are colored? ___8___

Look at the number of squares colored for the puppet.

How many squares are colored? ___6___

How many more children chose the Princess than the Puppet?

_____ more

1. Ask your classmates to select their favorite snack.
   Color to make a bar graph. Then answer the questions.

Yogurt									
Fruit									
	0	1	2	3	4	5	6	7	8	9

2. Which snack is the favorite? _____

3. How many children selected fruit? _____

Problem Solving: Make a Graph

The chart shows what kinds of
stickers the children like.
Use the bar graph to answer
the questions.

Favorite Stickers		
	Flower	2
	Bird	4
	Boat	7
	Dog	3

Our Favorite Stickers

	0	1	2	3	4	5	6	7	8
Flower									
Bird									
Boat									
Dog									

1. Which sticker do children like the most? _____

2. How many fewer children chose
   Flower stickers than Bird stickers? _____ fewer

3. **Number Sense**

   Which of the following shows the least favorite and the
   most favorite sticker?

   Ⓐ   dog and boat

   Ⓑ   flower and boat

   Ⓒ   flower and dog

   Ⓓ   boat and bird

Identifying Plane Shapes

Plane Shapes

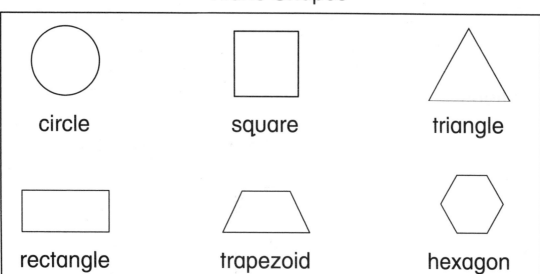

circle   square   triangle

rectangle   trapezoid   hexagon

Color the shapes that are the same.
Circle the name of the shapes you colored.

1.

square

triangle

2.

square

circle

3.

hexagon

trapezoid

Identifying Plane Shapes

1. Draw a rectangle.

2. Draw a square.

3. Draw a triangle.

4. Draw a hexagon.

Geometry

5. I am not a rectangle.
I am not a triangle.
What shape am I?

     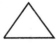

(A)   (B)   (C)   (D)

Algebra

6. Which shape comes next in the pattern?

      ___

 (A)   (B)   (C)   (D)

Problem Solving:
Make an Organized List

You can use pattern blocks to make another shape.

How many can fit in ? 2

How many can fit in ? 3

There are 3 ways you can make
this shape using pattern blocks.

Complete the organized list.

Ways to Make △▽			
	△	▱	⬯
Way 1	4	0	0
Way 2			
Way 3			

Problem Solving:
Make an Organized List

How many ways can you make
this shape using pattern blocks?

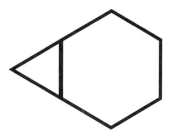

1. Make a list.

Ways to Make 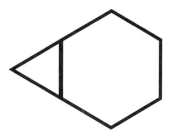				
Shapes I Used	⬡ (trapezoid)	⬡ (hexagon)	△	▱
Way 1				
Way 2				
Way 3				
Way 4				
Way 5				
Way 6				

Journal

2. How many ways can you use pattern blocks
to make a ▱? Explain.

Properties of Plane Shapes

Count the straight sides.	Count the corners.	
A triangle has ___3___ straight sides.	A triangle has ___3___ corners.	A circle has __0__ sides. A circle has __0__ corners.

Count the straight sides. Count the corners.

1. □

A square has ___4___ straight sides.

A square has ___4___ corners.

2. ▭

A rectangle has _____ straight sides.

A rectangle has _____ corners.

3. Draw a shape with more than 4 corners.

4. Draw a shape with more than 4 straight sides.

Name _____

Properties of Plane Shapes

1. Draw a shape with 4 corners.

2. Draw a shape with more than 4 straight sides.

3. Draw a shape with 3 sides and 3 corners.

4. I have 4 sides and 4 corners. Which shape am I?

Ⓐ circle

Ⓑ trapezoid

Ⓒ hexagon

Ⓓ triangle

Reasoning

5. Here is the way Brian sorted some plane shapes.

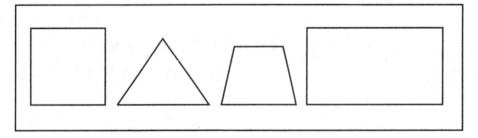

Circle the question Brian might have asked.

Does it have fewer than 5 corners?

Does it have more than 5 straight sides?

Building with Shapes

You can use pattern blocks to make a picture.

Make a candle.

Then write how many of each shape you used.

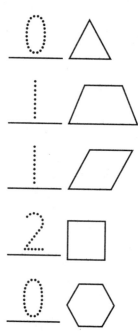

_0_ △

_1_ ▱ (trapezoid)

_1_ ▱ (parallelogram)

_2_ □

_0_ ⬡

Use pattern blocks to make a picture.
Write how many of each shape you used.

I. The picture is a ___tree___.

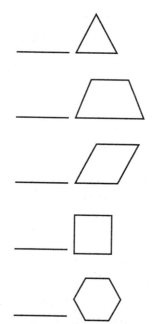

___ △

___ ▱

___ ▱

___ □

___ ⬡

Building with Shapes

Use pattern blocks to make a picture.
Write how many of each shape you used.

1.

_____ △

_____ ⏢

_____ ▱

_____ □

_____ ⬡

Spatial Thinking

2. José is making a picture
   of a bunny.
   He is missing one block.
   Which block is missing?

Ⓐ   Ⓑ   Ⓒ   Ⓓ

Making New Shapes
from Shapes

Give 3 ways you can make this
shape using pattern blocks.

You need to find all the ways that
pattern blocks can make the shape.

A list can help you keep track.

Ways to Make △			
Shapes I Used	△	△	⬭
Way 1	1	0	0
Way 2	0	3	0
Way 3	0	1	1

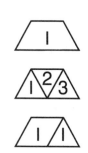

Did you find 3 ways? How do you know?

Give 3 ways you can make this shape
using pattern blocks. Complete the list.

Ways to Make ⬭			
Shapes I Used	△	⬭	△
Way 1	1	0	1
Way 2			
Way 3			

Making New Shapes from Shapes

Use pattern blocks or Teaching Tool 22 to make each shape.
Draw the shapes you used.

Make This Shape	Use This Shape	Draw the Shapes
1. ◯	◠	
2. (trapezoid)	△	

3. Mark the number that tells how
   many △ you need to make a ⬡.

4	5	6	7
Ⓐ	Ⓑ	Ⓒ	Ⓓ

4. **Writing in Math** Use pattern blocks to make a new shape.
   Trace the blocks you used below.

Identifying Solid Figures

These shapes are solid figures.

sphere   cone   cylinder   cube   rectangular prism

Color the spheres red. Color the cones blue.
Color the cylinders green. Color the cubes orange.
Color the rectangular prisms yellow.

I.

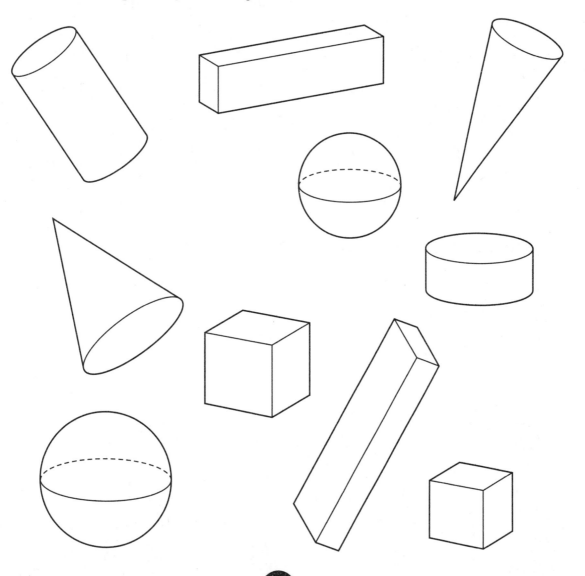

Identifying Solid Figures

1. Color each solid figure below.

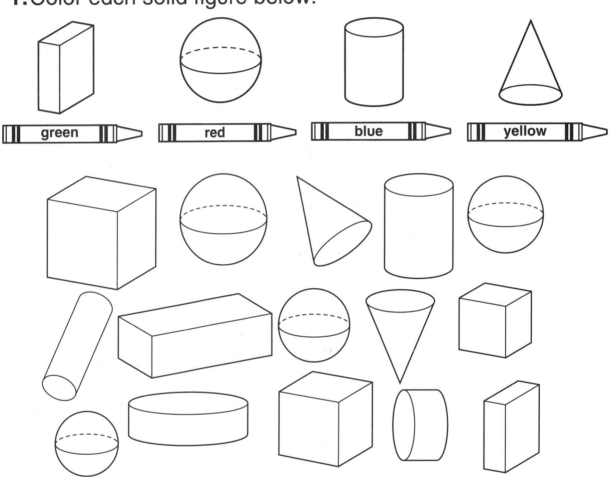

green   red   blue   yellow

2. Now put an X on each cube.

Algebra

3. Which solid figure comes next?

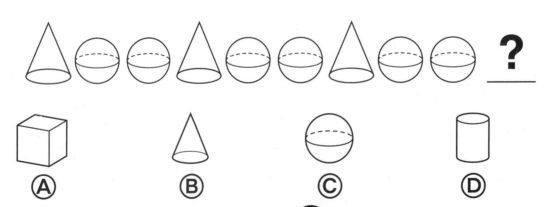

Ⓐ   Ⓑ   Ⓒ   Ⓓ

Flat Surfaces and Vertices

These solid figures have **flat surfaces.**

 cone   cylinder

 rectangular prism   cube

These solid figures have **vertices** or corners.

Use solid figures to complete the table.

Solid Figure	Number of Flat Surfaces	Number of Vertices (Corners)
1. cube	6	8
2. cone		
3. rectangular prism		
4. cylinder		

Flat Surfaces and Vertices

Circle the solid figure that answers each question.

1. Which solid figure has 2 flat surfaces and 0 vertices?

2. Which solid figure has 0 flat surfaces and 0 vertices?

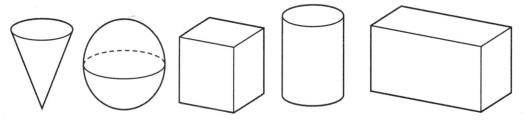

3. Which solid figures have 6 flat surfaces and 8 vertices?

Reasoning

4. Mark the solid figure that answers the question.

I have I flat surface. I have I vertex.
Which solid figure am I?

Ⓐ

Ⓑ

Ⓒ

Ⓓ

Name _____

Sorting Solid Figures

You can sort solid figures in many different ways.

Some figures have flat
surfaces and cannot roll.

Some have flat surfaces and can roll.

Some have vertices.

Some have no vertices.

Circle the solid figure that follows the sorting rule.

1. It has all flat surfaces.

2. It has no flat surfaces.

3. It can roll.

- -

4. Circle the 2 figures
that have flat surfaces
and curves.

Sorting Solid Figures

Read the sorting rule.
Circle the solid figures that follow the rule.

1. 1 flat surface

2. 8 vertices

3. 2 flat surfaces

4. 6 flat surfaces

5. 0 vertices

- -

6. Which rule tells how these solid figures are alike?

    Ⓐ   3 vertices

    Ⓑ   4 flat surfaces

    Ⓒ   5 vertices

    Ⓓ   6 flat surfaces

Building with Solid Figures

You can build an object by using solid figures.

rectangular prism   cylinder   sphere   cone   cube   pyramid

| Build a tower. | **Step 1:** Start with a rectangular prism. | **Step 2:** Put a cone on top. |

Build each object. Draw the solid figures.
Then write the solid figures you used to build the object.

| 1. Build a lamp post. | **Step 1:** Start with a _____. | **Step 2:** Put a _____ on top. |
| 2. Build a tree. | Start with a _____. | Put a _____ on top. |

Building with Solid Figures

Look at the object.
Write how many of each solid figure is used
to make the object.

1.

____ ____ ____ ____

2.

____ ____ ____ ____

3.

____ ____ ____ ____

Spatial Thinking

4. Kim used these 2 solid figures
to make an object.
Which object did Kim make?

    Ⓒ Ⓓ

Problem Solving: Use Reasoning

All of these shapes are triangles.
Circle the words that are true of all triangles.

Look at each of the sentences below and then look at the triangles.

Circle the words that do match all the triangles.

All triangles:

> For the first sentence, think: I can see a shape that is not gray but is still a triangle, so I do not circle this.

are gray

(have 3 straight sides)

(have 3 corners)

have a flat bottom

I. All of these shapes are cubes. Circle the words that are true of all cubes.
All cubes:

are gray

(have 6 flat surfaces)

are big

(have 8 vertices)

---

2. All of these shapes are circles. Circle the words that are true of all circles.
All circles:

have 0 straight sides

have 0 vertices

are big

are white

Problem Solving: Use Reasoning

1. All of these shapes are rectangles.
   Circle the words that are true of all
   rectangles.
   All rectangles:

   have 4 sides

   have 4 corners

   are white

   have the longest side at the bottom

   are big

2. All of these shapes are rectangular prisms.
   Circle the words that are true of all rectangular prisms.
   All rectangular prisms:

   are white

   are big

   have 8 vertices

   are gray

   have 6 flat surfaces

3. Which shows something that
   is true of all cylinders?
   All cylinders:

   Ⓐ   are gray

   Ⓑ   are small

   Ⓒ   have 2 flat surfaces

   Ⓓ   have a flat surface at the top

Making Equal Parts

This apple pie is divided into equal parts.

Each part is the same size.

There are ___4___ equal parts.

This apple pie is **not** divided into equal parts.

Each part is **not** the same size.

There are ___0___ equal parts.

Write the number of equal parts on each shape.

1.

   There are ___4___ equal parts.

2.

   There are _____ equal parts.

3.

   There are _____ equal parts.

4.

   There are _____ equal parts.

5.

   There are _____ equal parts.

6.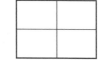

   There are _____ equal parts.

Making Equal Parts

Write how many equal parts the shape has.
If the parts are not equal, write 0.

I.

_____ equal parts

2.

_____ equal parts

3.

_____ equal parts

4.

_____ equal parts

5.

_____ equal parts

6.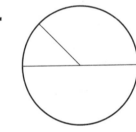

_____ equal parts

Journal

7. Draw straight lines to divide these
shapes into the equal parts listed.

2 equal parts

4 equal parts

2 equal parts

Describing Equal Parts of Whole Objects

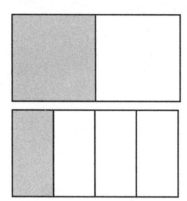

This rectangle has 2 equal parts.
1 out of 2 equal parts is shaded.

1 out of 4 equal parts is shaded.

---

1. Circle the shape that shows 1 out of 2 equal parts shaded.

....

2. Circle the shape that shows 1 out of 4 equal parts shaded.

....

3. Circle the shape that shows 3 out of 4 equal parts shaded.

Describing Equal Parts of Whole Objects

Color the given number of equal parts in each shape.

1.

1 out of 4 equal parts

2.

3 out of 4 equal parts

3.

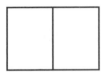

1 out of 2 equal parts

4.

2 out of 4 equal parts

Spatial Thinking

5. Which picture shows 2 out of 4 equal parts shaded?

Ⓐ

Ⓑ

Ⓒ

Ⓓ

Number Sense

6. How many fourths equal one whole?

Ⓐ 4

Ⓑ 3

Ⓒ 2

Ⓓ 1

Making Halves and Fourths of Rectangles and Circles

You can divide a figure into equal parts.

Two of the *halves* make the whole circle.

Four of the **quarters** make the whole rectangle.

Each part is called a **half**. A **half** of the circle is gray.

The rectangle is divided into **quarters.** Each part is called a **quarter.**

Circle the shape that shows one half shaded gray.

1.

2.

Circle the shape that shows one quarter striped.

3.

4.

---

5. Julie colors half of the circle green. How many pieces does she need to color?
Color the parts.
Write the number.

 ____

Making Halves and Fourths of Rectangles and Circles

Color the shapes so that half of each shape is blue.

1. 　　**2.** 　　**3.**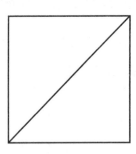

Color the shapes so that a quarter of each shape is orange.

4. 　　**5.** 　　**6.**

7. Marco cut this square into halves. Draw a line to cut it into fourths.

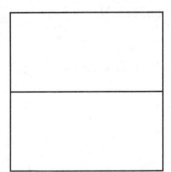

Problem Solving: Draw a Picture

You can draw a picture to solve a problem.

Mario's pizza has 4 equal parts.

2 of the parts have mushrooms on them.

What part of the pizza has mushrooms?

First, draw Mario's pizza.

Then draw mushrooms on 2 of the parts.

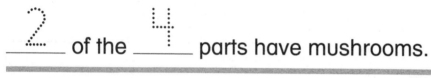 of the _____ parts have mushrooms.

1. Julia's flag has 2 equal parts.
   1 of the parts has stars on it.
   What part of the flag has stars?

   Draw a picture of Julia's flag.

   _____ out of _____ parts has stars.

2. Jake's flag has 4 equal parts.
   3 of the parts are red.
   What part of the flag is red?

   Draw a picture of Jake's flag.

   _____ out of _____ parts are red.

Problem Solving: Draw a Picture

Read each story.
Draw a picture.
Write the number.

1. Fred's quilt has 2 equal parts.
   1 of the parts is blue.
   What part of Fred's quilt is blue?

   _____ out of _____ parts

2. Dale's flag has 4 equal parts.
   3 of the parts are yellow.
   What part of Dale's flag is yellow?

   _____ out of _____ parts

3. Reasoning Tim's pizza has
   4 equal parts.
   He eats 2 of the parts.
   How many parts are left for
   his friends?

   1   2   3   4
   Ⓐ   Ⓑ   Ⓒ   Ⓓ

Name _____

Building 1,000

Remember.

10 ones = _____ ten

10 tens = _____ hundred

10 hundreds = _____ thousand

Count by 100s to count hundreds.

Color the models to show the hundreds.

1. 2 hundreds
    200

2. 3 hundreds
    300

3. 1 hundred
    100

4. 5 hundreds
    500

Name _____

Building 1,000

Write how many. Use models if needed.

1.

100 less is

_____.

_____

100 more is

_____.

2.

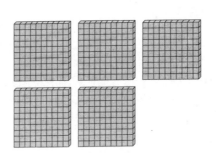

100 less is

_____.

_____

100 more is

_____.

3. Each bag has 100 pretzels.

There are 8 bags.

How many pretzels are there in all?

80	100	500	800
Ⓐ	Ⓑ	Ⓒ	Ⓓ

4. Number Sense Write the number that comes next:

100 200 300 400 500 600 700 800 900 _____

How many hundred flats would you need to show it?

_____ hundred flats

Counting Hundreds, Tens, and Ones

Use models and your workmat to sort and count.

First, put the hundreds models on your mat.
Next, put the tens models on your mat.
Then, put the ones models on your mat.

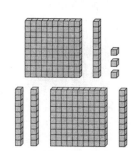

Write the number of hundreds, tens, and ones.

Hundreds	Tens	Ones
2	4	3

Write the numbers.
Use models and your workmat if needed.

I.

Hundreds	Tens	Ones
1	5	6

2.

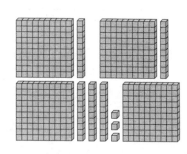

Hundreds	Tens	Ones

3. Number Sense How many hundreds are in 217? _____

Counting Hundreds, Tens, and Ones

Write the numbers. Use models and your workmat if needed.

1.

Hundreds	Tens	Ones

2.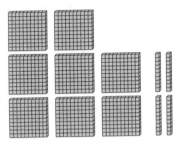

Hundreds	Tens	Ones

3.

Hundreds	Tens	Ones

4.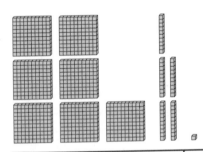

Hundreds	Tens	Ones

5. Reasonableness Kyra wrote **65** to match the model.

What mistake did she make?

_____

_____

What is the correct number to match the model?

650	605	506	56
Ⓐ	Ⓑ	Ⓒ	Ⓓ

Reading and Writing Numbers to 1,000

Expanded form uses plus signs to show hundreds, tens, and ones.

200 + 60 + 4

You can draw models to show expanded form.

The **number word** is two hundred sixty-four.

The **standard form** is

264.

Draw models to show the expanded form.
Write the number in standard form.

1. 400 + 30 + 8   four hundred thirty-eight

_____

2. 300 + 70 + 2   three hundred seventy-two

_____

3. Write the number in expanded   five hundred fourteen
and standard form.

_____ + _____ + _____   _____

Reading and Writing Numbers to 1,000

Circle the models to match the expanded form.
Then write the standard form.

1. 200 + 70 + 5

two hundred
seventy-five

275

2. 100 + 40 + 0

one hundred
forty

_____

3. 300 + 60 + 2

three hundred
sixty-two

_____

4. 329 cars are parked in a parking lot.

What is the expanded form of 329?

Ⓐ 200 + 90 + 3

Ⓑ 200 + 20 + 9

Ⓒ 300 + 20 + 9

Ⓓ 300 + 90 + 2

5. Reasoning What is the greatest number you can make using these digits?

5   7   2

Ⓐ 257

Ⓑ 572

Ⓒ 725

Ⓓ 752

Name _____

Comparing Numbers

Compare the digits with the greatest place value first.

125   243

100 is __less than__ 200. So, 125 ⬤< 243.

If the hundreds are equal, compare the tens.

243   217

40 is __greater than__ 10. So, 243 ⬤> 217.

If the tens are equal, compare the ones.

217   216

7 is __greater than__ 6. So, 217 ⬤> 216.

Compare.
Write <, >, or =.

1. 341 ◯ 432

2. 890 ◯ 880

3. 621 ◯ 639

4. 546 ◯ 546

Comparing Numbers

Compare. Write **greater than**, **less than**, or **equal to**.
Then write >, <, or =.

1. 157 is ___less than___ 214.   157 $<$ 214

2. 600 is _____ 598.   600 $\bigcirc$ 598

3. 771 is _____ 771.   771 $\bigcirc$ 771

4. This week, 261 fans watched a soccer game.
Last week, 216 fans watched a soccer game.
Which comparison is correct?

   Ⓐ 216 = 261

   Ⓑ 216 > 261

   Ⓒ 261 < 216

   Ⓓ 216 < 261

5. Spatial Thinking Circle hundreds, tens, and
ones to show your answer.

This number is less than 200. The ones digit is
5 less than 10. The tens digit is 2 more than the
ones digit. What is the number?

_____

Adding Two-Digit Numbers

Remember the steps for adding:

| **Step 1:** | **Step 2:** | **Step 3:** |
| Add the ones. | Regroup if you need to. | Add the tens. |

34 + 27 = ?
Regroup 11 ones
as 1 ten and 1 one.

Tens	Ones
1	
3	4
+ 2	7
6	1

12 + 36 = ?
You do not
need to regroup
8 ones.

Tens	Ones
1	2
+ 3	6
4	8

Write the addition problem. Find the sum.

1.

15 + 26

Tens	Ones
1	
1	5
+ 2	6
4	1

37 + 12

Tens	Ones
3	7
+ 1	

28 + 15

Tens	Ones
2	8
+	

35 + 36

Tens	Ones
+	

2. Algebra Begin with 24. Find the number
that gives you a sum of 43. Use cubes
to help you.

The number is _____.

Tens	Ones
2	4
+	
4	3

Name _____

Adding Two-Digit Numbers

Write the addition problem. Find the sum.

1. 36 + 21

Tens	Ones
3	6
+ 2	1

2. 31 + 19

Tens	Ones
+	

3. 63 + 19

Tens	Ones
+	

4. 56 + 34

Tens	Ones
+	

5. 63 + 26

Tens	Ones
+	

6. 54 + 28

Tens	Ones
+	

7. 68 + 29

Tens	Ones
+	

8. 33 + 47

Tens	Ones
+	

9. Ryan has a stack of 52 dimes and a stack of 29 dimes. How many dimes does he have in all?

Ⓐ 54
Ⓑ 59
Ⓒ 71
Ⓓ 81

10. Estimation One jar has 22 marbles. Another jar has 28 marbles. About how many marbles are in both jars?

Ⓐ about 40
Ⓑ about 50
Ⓒ about 60
Ⓓ about 70

Name _____

Subtracting Two-Digit Numbers

Remember the steps for subtracting.

Step 1
Think: Are there enough ones to subtract?

Step 2
Regroup the ones if you need to. Subtract.

Step 3
Subtract the tens.

Write the problems in the frames. Find the difference.

38 − 13

Regroup?   Yes   No

54 − 17

Regroup?   Yes   No

Write the problems in the frames. Find the difference.

1.   37 − 14   43 − 26   66 − 37   73 − 25

Tens	Ones
3	7
1	4
2	3

Tens	Ones

Tens	Ones

Tens	Ones

2. **Number Sense** Write a number to make this a subtraction with regrouping problem.

Tens	Ones
− 2	8

Subtracting Two-Digit Numbers

Write the subtraction problem. Find the difference.

1. 64 − 39

Tens	Ones
□	□
−	

2. 47 − 18

Tens	Ones
□	□
−	

3. 84 − 57

Tens	Ones
□	□
−	

4. 56 − 29

Tens	Ones
□	□
−	

5. 72 − 44

Tens	Ones
□	□
−	

6. 34 − 16

Tens	Ones
□	□
−	

7. 96 − 48

Tens	Ones
□	□
−	

8. 81 − 63

Tens	Ones
□	□
−	

9. Stan has 63 buttons. Chad has 47 buttons. How many more buttons does Stan have than Chad?

Ⓐ 26

Ⓑ 24

Ⓒ 23

Ⓓ 16

10. Number Sense Use each number only once. Write and solve the subtraction problem with the greatest difference.

2 3 5 6

Tens	Ones
□	□
□	□
−	

Using Addition to Check Subtraction

When you subtract,
you start with the whole.
Then you take part away.
The other part is left.

37 [Whole]
− 12 [Part]
25 [Part]

Tens	Ones

To check your work,
add to put the parts
back together.
Your answer should
be the whole.

25 [Part]
+ 12 [Part]
37 [Whole]

Tens	Ones

and   and

Subtract. Check your answer by adding.

1.

Tens	Ones
3	3
− 2	1
1	2

12
+ 21
33

2.

Tens	Ones
5	6
−	7

3.

Tens	Ones
3	4
− 1	9

4.

Tens	Ones
6	3
− 3	7

Name _____

Using Addition to Check Subtraction

Subtract. Check your answer by adding. Write the missing part.

1.

$$\begin{array}{r} 62 \\ -\ 14 \\ \hline \end{array}$$

2.

$$\begin{array}{r} 83 \\ -\ 29 \\ \hline \end{array}$$

3.

$$\begin{array}{r} 73 \\ -\ 37 \\ \hline \end{array}$$

4.

$$\begin{array}{r} 48 \\ -\ 27 \\ \hline \end{array}$$

5.

$$\begin{array}{r} 94 \\ -\ 37 \\ \hline \end{array}$$

6.

$$\begin{array}{r} 75 \\ -\ 17 \\ \hline \end{array}$$

7. Betty has 48 moon stickers and 63 star stickers. How many more star stickers than moon stickers does she have?

Ⓐ 15

Ⓑ 19

Ⓒ 23

Ⓓ 27

8. Algebra Write the number that makes each number sentence true.

$60 - 20 = 20 +$ _____

$50 - 40 = 10 +$ _____

$70 - 30 = 10 +$ _____

$80 - 40 = 30 +$ _____

Name _____

Inches

Use a ruler to measure inches.

To measure to the nearest inch, look at the halfway mark between inches. If the object is longer, use the greater number. If the object is shorter, use the lesser number.

The bead is about

____ inch long.

The bead is about

_2_ inches long.

1.Journal Find something in the classroom to measure in inches. Draw the object and write the measurement to the nearest inch.

Estimate the height or length.
Then use a ruler to measure.

2. length of a pencil

3. height of a book

	Estimate	Measure
	about ____ inches	about ____ inches
	about ____ inches	about ____ inches

Name _____

Inches

Estimate the length of each object.
Then use a ruler to measure.

1.

Estimate: about _____ inches

Measure: about _____ inches

2.

Estimate: about _____ inches

Measure: about _____ inches

3. Estimate: about _____ inches

Measure: about _____ inches

4.

Estimate: about _____ inches

Measure: about _____ inches

5. **Reasonableness.** Measure the length of the straw in inches.
   About how long is the straw?

Ⓐ about 5 inches   © about 7 inches

Ⓑ about 6 inches   Ⓓ about 8 inches

Centimeters

Use a ruler to measure centimeters.

To measure to the nearest centimeter, look at the halfway mark between centimeters. If the object is longer, use the greater number. If the object is shorter, use the smaller number.

CENTIMETERS

The paper clip is about

_3_ centimeters.

This part of the door is about

_100_ centimeters.

---

1. **Writing in Math** Find something in the classroom to measure in centimeters. Draw the object and write the measurement to the nearest centimeter.

Estimate the height or length.
Then use a ruler to measure.

2. height of a book

3. length of a tape dispenser

	Estimate	Measure
	about _____ centimeters	about _____ centimeters
	about _____ centimeters	about _____ centimeters

Centimeters

Estimate the length of each object.
Then use a ruler to measure.

1.

Estimate: about _____ cm

Measure: about _____ cm

2.

Estimate: about _____ cm

Measure: about _____ cm

3.

Estimate: about _____ cm

Measure: about _____ cm

4. Look at the spoon. Measure the length of the spoon in centimeters. About how long is the spoon?

Ⓐ about 10 centimeters Ⓒ about 16 centimeters

Ⓑ about 13 centimeters Ⓓ about 18 centimeters

5. **Spatial Thinking** Choose the object that is about 4 centimeters long.

Ⓐ   Ⓒ

Ⓑ   Ⓓ

Inches, Feet, and Yards

The stamp is about 1 inch long.	The book is about 1 foot long.	The table is about 1 yard long.

About how long or tall is each object? Circle the answer.

1.

(about 1 inch)

about 1 foot

about 1 yard

2.

about 1 inch

about 1 foot

about 1 yard

3.

about 1 inch

about 1 foot

about 1 yard

4.

about 1 inch

about 1 foot

about 1 yard

5. Estimation About how tall is the piece of paper?

about 1 inch   about 2 inches   about 2 feet

Name _____

Inches, Feet, and Yards

Circle the object that is about each length.

1. an inch

2. a foot

3. a yard

4. Measure from your fingertips to your elbow.

Estimate

about _____ inches

Measure

about _____ inches

5. Ingrid measures the length of a hockey stick. She says it is _____ long. Which measurement did she use?

Ⓐ 4 inches

Ⓑ 1 foot

Ⓒ 4 feet

Ⓓ 4 yards

6. Reasonableness Which is the best measurement for the height of the water bottle?

Ⓐ about 1 inch

Ⓑ about 9 inches

Ⓒ about 9 feet

Ⓓ about 9 yards